The
BRAINTEASERS
Number
Puzzles
Book

KT-417-628

THIS IS A CARLTON BOOK

This edition published 1998 for
Parragon Book Service Ltd
Unit 13–17 Avonbridge Trading Estate,
Atlantic Road, Avonmouth
Bristol BS11 9QD

Text and design copyright © Carlton Books Limited 1998

All rights reserved. No part of this publication may be
reproduced, stored in a retrieval system, or transmitted
in any form or by any means without the prior written
permission of the publisher, nor be otherwise circulated
in any form of binding or cover other than that in which
it is published and without a similar condition being
imposed in the subsequent purchaser.

ISBN 1 75252 752 5

Printed and bound by Firmin-Didot (France)
Group Herissey
N° d'impression : 43559

The
BRAINTEASERS
Number
Puzzles
Book

SIENA

INTRODUCTION

There is every kind of number puzzle present in this book. Your number skills will be tested to the limit with magic number squares, series puzzles, grid problems, matrix puzzles, balances, logic problems and the list goes on and on. There are over 250 number problems covering these pages, so they should keep you busy for quite some time.

Take this handy book anywhere with you and you can entertain yourself while exercising those brain cells and increasing your numeracy skills. Some of these problems will involve a bit of lateral and logical thinking which should give you a good mental workout.

These are fun puzzles, some of which are on the easy side others which are more testing. No special skills are needed beyond common sense, basic literacy, and a tenacious will not to give up. So more than anything, enjoy!

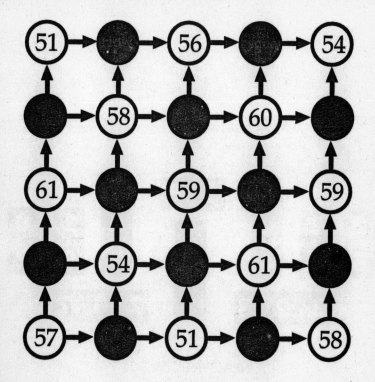

NUMBER PUZZLE 1

Move from the bottom left-hand corner to
the top right-hand corner following the arrows.
Add the numbers on your route together.
If each black spot is worth minus 23, how many
different routes are there to score 188?

ANSWER 62

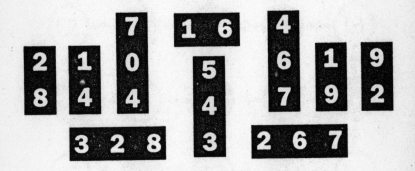

NUMBER PUZZLE 2

Place the tiles in a square to give some five-figure numbers. When this has been done accurately the same five numbers can be read both down and across. How does the finished square look?

ANSWER 10

NUMBER PUZZLE 3

Start in the middle circle and move from circle to
touching circle. Collect the four numbers which
will total 70. Once a route has been found return to
the middle circle and start again.

If a route can be found, which obeys the
above rules but follows both a clockwise and an
anticlockwise path, it is treated as two
different routes.

How many different ways are there?

ANSWER 103

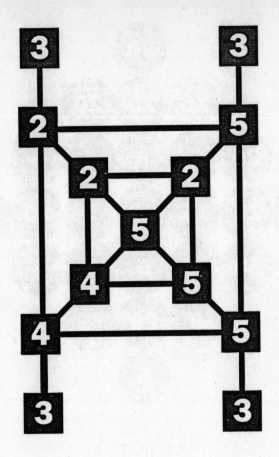

NUMBER PUZZLE 4

Start at any corner and follow the lines.
Add up the first four numbers you meet
and then add on the corner number.
What is the highest you can score?

ANSWER 222

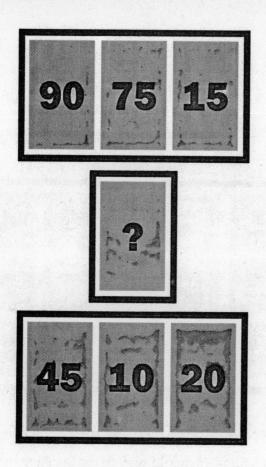

NUMBER PUZZLE 5

Place in the middle box a number larger than 1.
If the number is the correct one, all the other
numbers can be divided by it without leaving any
remainder. What is the number?

ANSWER 235

NUMBER PUZZLE 6

Which number should replace the question mark in
the diagram?

ANSWER 51

NUMBER PUZZLE 7

You have four shots with each go to score 75.
Aim at this target and work out how many
different ways there are to make the score. Assume
each shot scores and once four numbers have been
used the same four cannot be used again in
another order.
How many are there?

ANSWER 92

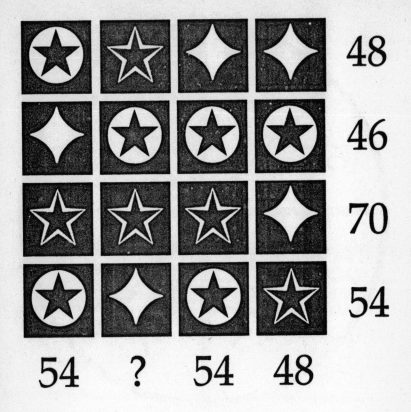

48

46

70

54

54   ?   54   48

NUMBER PUZZLE 8

The contents of each box has a value. The total of the values is shown alongside a row or beneath a column. Which number should replace the question mark?

ANSWER 40

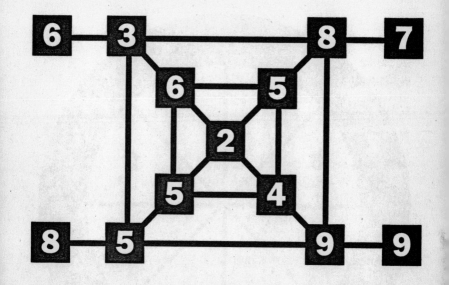

NUMBER PUZZLE 9

Start at any corner number and collect another four
numbers by following the paths shown. Add the
five numbers together.
What is the highest total which can be attained?

ANSWER 82

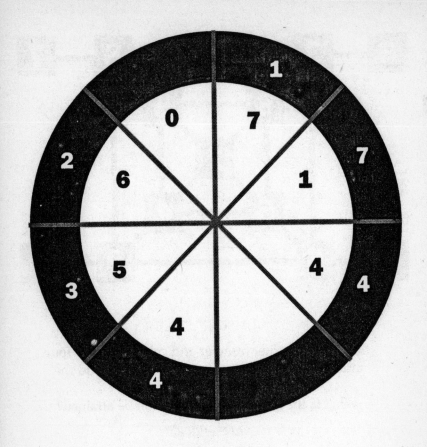

NUMBER PUZZLE 10

Each slice of this cake adds up to the same number.
All the numbers going round the cake total 32.
Which numbers should appear in the blanks?

ANSWER 203

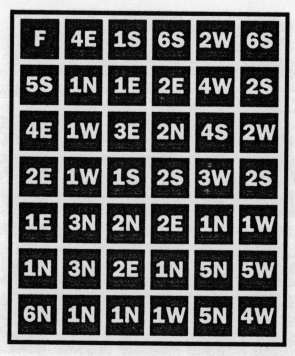

F	4E	1S	6S	2W	6S
5S	1N	1E	2E	4W	2S
4E	1W	3E	2N	4S	2W
2E	1W	1S	2S	3W	2S
1E	3N	2N	2E	1N	1W
1N	3N	2E	1N	5N	5W
6N	1N	1N	1W	5N	4W

NUMBER PUZZLE 11

Here is an unusual safe. Each of the buttons must
be pressed only once in the correct order to open it.
The last button is marked F. The number of moves
and the direction is marked on each button.
Thus 1N would mean one move north, whilst 1W
would mean one move to the west. Which button is
the first you must press? Here's a clue: it can be
found on the middle row.

ANSWER 241

5	4	6	3	8
6	2	7	4	4
4	3	6	5	3
5	4	5	6	4
3	5	4	7	5

NUMBER PUZZLE 12

Move from square to adjacent square either
vertically or horizontally. Begin at the bottom
left-hand square and end at the top right-hand
square. Collect nine numbers and total them.
How many different ways are there to total 38?

ANSWER 30

A B C D E

A	B	C	D	E
6	3	3	9	6
5	4	1	9	8
7	1	6	8	
8	1	7	9	
4	3	1	7	6

NUMBER PUZZLE 13

There is a relationship between the columns of numbers in this diagram. The letters above the grid are there to help you. Which number should be placed in the empty squares?

ANSWER 72

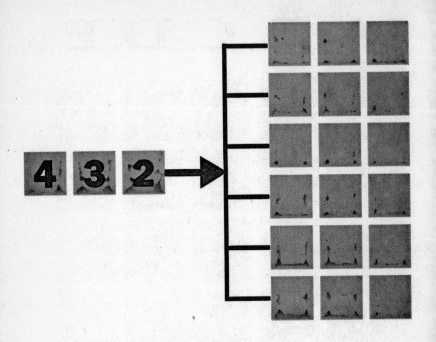

NUMBER PUZZLE 14

Place six three digit numbers of 100 plus at the end
of 432 so that six numbers of six digits are
produced. When each number is divided by 151 six
whole numbers can be found.
Which numbers should be placed in the grid?

ANSWER 20

NUMBER PUZZLE 15

Each row, column and five-figure diagonal line
in this diagram must total 85. Four different
numbers must be used, as many times as necessary,
to achieve this.
What are the numbers?

ANSWER 61

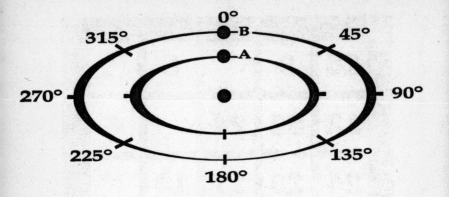

NUMBER PUZZLE 16

Two planets are in line with each other and the
sun. The outer planet will orbit the sun every
twelve years. The inner planet takes three years.
Both move in a clockwise direction. When will they
next form a straight line with each other and the
sun? The diagram should help you.

ANSWER 9

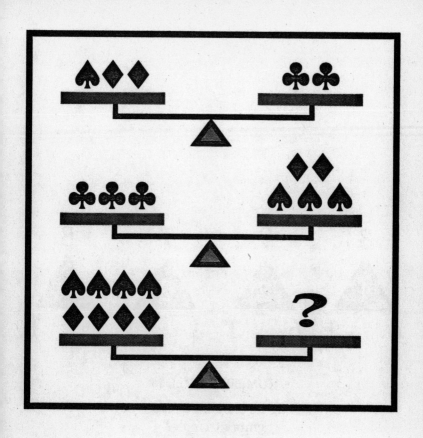

NUMBER PUZZLE 17

The top two scales are in perfect balance.
How many clubs will be needed to balance the
bottom set?

ANSWER 102

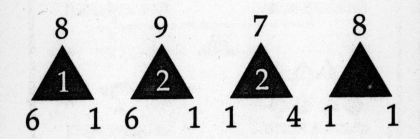

8
1
6 1

9
2
6 1

7
2
1 4

8

1 1

NUMBER PUZZLE 18

Which figure should be placed in the
empty triangle?

ANSWER 50

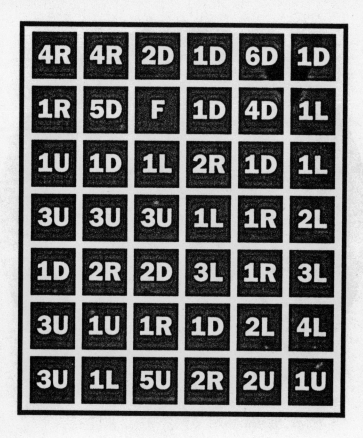

4R	4R	2D	1D	6D	1D
1R	5D	F	1D	4D	1L
1U	1D	1L	2R	1D	1L
3U	3U	3U	1L	1R	2L
1D	2R	2D	3L	1R	3L
3U	1U	1R	1D	2L	4L
3U	1L	5U	2R	2U	1U

NUMBER PUZZLE 19

Here is an unusual safe. Each of the buttons must
be pressed once only in the correct order to open it.
The last button is always marked F. The number of
moves and the direction is marked on each button.
Thus 1U would mean one move up
whilst 1L would mean one move to the left.
Which button is the first you must press.

ANSWER 91

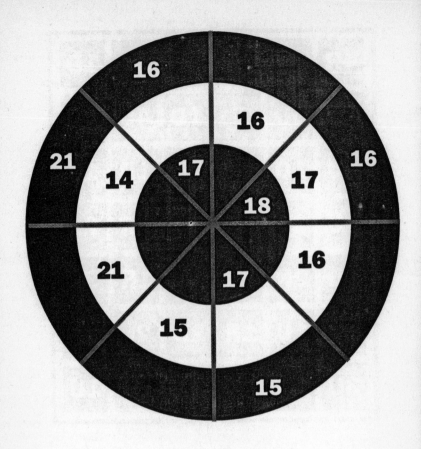

NUMBER PUZZLE 20

Complete the grid in such a way that each segment
of three numbers totals the same.
When this has been done correctly each of the three
concentric circles of eight numbers will produce
three identical totals.
Now complete the diagram.

ANSWER 39

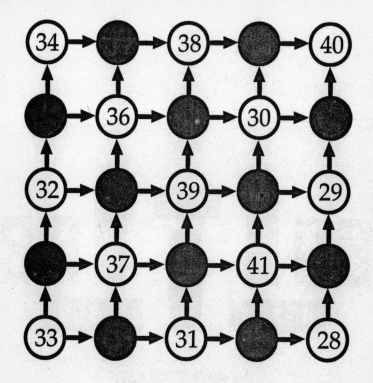

NUMBER PUZZLE 21

Move from the bottom left-hand corner to the top right-hand corner following the arrows. Add the numbers on your route together. If each black spot is worth minus 8, how many different routes are there to score 155?

ANSWER 81

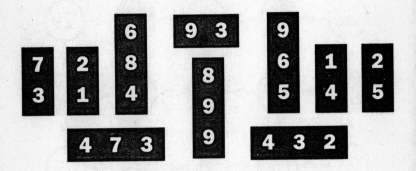

NUMBER PUZZLE 22

Place the tiles in a square to give some five-figure numbers. When this has been done accurately the same five numbers can be read both down and across. How does the finished square look?

ANSWER 29

NUMBER PUZZLE 23

Start in the middle circle and move from circle to touching circle. Collect the four numbers which will total 86. Once a route has been found return to the middle circle and start again.

If a route can be found, which obeys the above rules but follows both a clockwise and an anti-clockwise path, it is treated as two different routes. How many different ways are there?

ANSWER 71

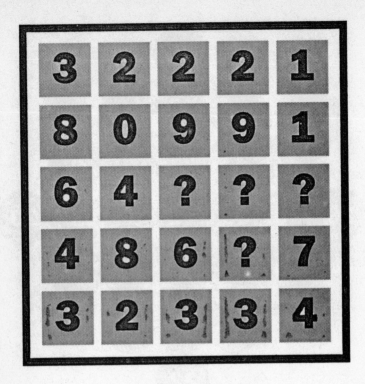

NUMBER PUZZLE 24

Which number should replace the question marks
in the diagram?

ANSWER 19

NUMBER PUZZLE 25

You have four shots with each go to score 51. Aim at this target and work out how many different ways there are to make the score. Assume each shot scores and once four numbers have been used the same four cannot be used again in another order. How many are there?

ANSWER 8

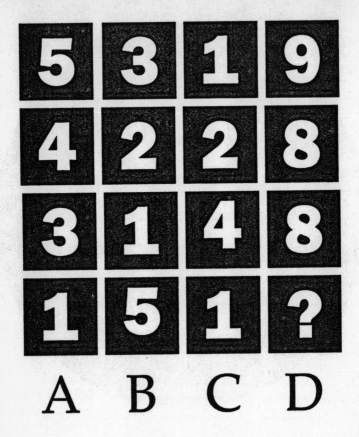

A B C D

NUMBER PUZZLE 26

The numbers in column D are linked in
some way to those in A, B and C. What number
should replace the question mark?

ANSWER 219

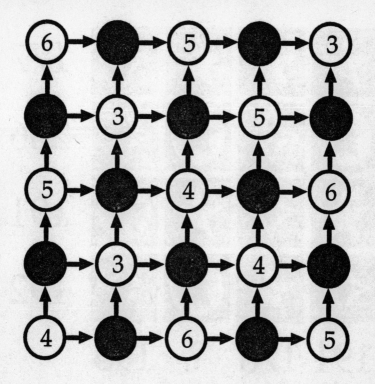

NUMBER PUZZLE 27

Move from the bottom left-hand 4 to the top
right-hand 3 adding together all five numbers.
Each black circle is worth minus 1 and this should
be taken away from your total each time you meet
one. What is the highest total you can find?

ANSWER 258

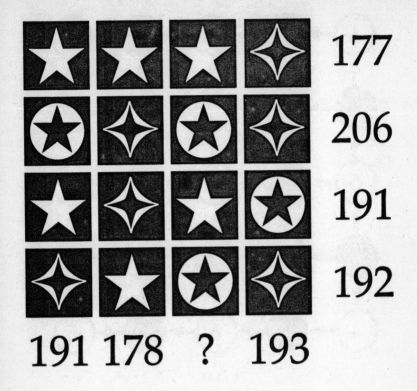

177

206

191

192

191 178 ? 193

NUMBER PUZZLE 28

The contents of each box has a value. The total of
the values is shown alongside a row or beneath a
column. Which number should replace the
question mark?

ANSWER 60

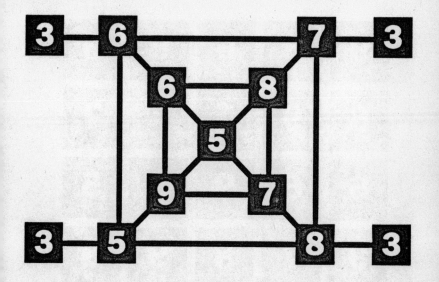

NUMBER PUZZLE 29

Start at any corner number and collect another four
numbers by following the paths shown. Add the
five numbers together.
How many times can you score 27?

ANSWER 101

NUMBER PUZZLE 30

Move from square to adjacent square either vertically or horizontally. Begin at the bottom left-hand square and end at the top right-hand square. Collect nine numbers and total them. How many different ways are there to total 66?

ANSWER 49

A B C D E

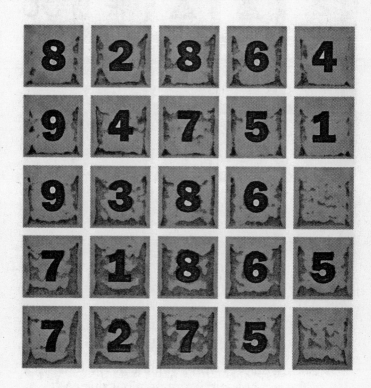

A	B	C	D	E
8	2	8	6	4
9	4	7	5	1
9	3	8	6	
7	1	8	6	5
7	2	7	5	

NUMBER PUZZLE 31

There is a relationship between the columns of numbers in this diagram. The letters above the grid are there to help you. Which number should be placed in the empty squares?

ANSWER 90

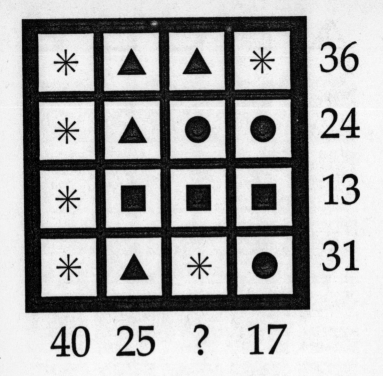

NUMBER PUZZLE 32

Each symbol is worth a number. The total
of the symbols can be found alongside each
row and column. What number should
replace the question mark?

ANSWER 215

NUMBER PUZZLE 33

Start at the middle 2 and move from circle to touching circle. Collect three numbers and add them to the 2. How many different routes are there to make a total of 12?

ANSWER 264

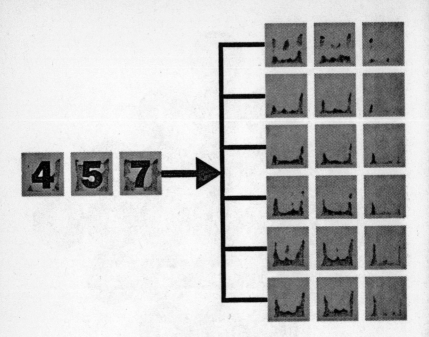

NUMBER PUZZLE 34

Place six three digit numbers of 100 plus at the end of 457 so that six numbers of six digits are produced. When each number is divided by 55.5 six whole numbers can be found. Which numbers should be placed in the grid?

ANSWER 38

NUMBER PUZZLE 35

Each row, column and five-figure diagonal line in this diagram must total 80. Three different numbers must be used, as many times as necessary, to achieve this.

What are the numbers?

ANSWER 80

NUMBER PUZZLE 36

Divide up the box using four lines so that each shape adds up to the same. How is this done?

ANSWER 236

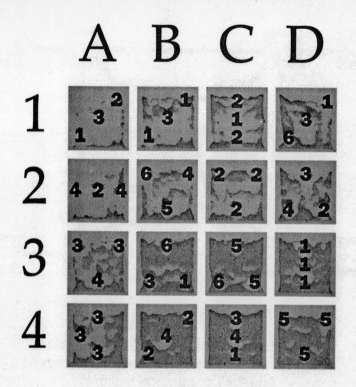

NUMBER PUZZLE 37

Which squares contain the same numbers?

ANSWER 213

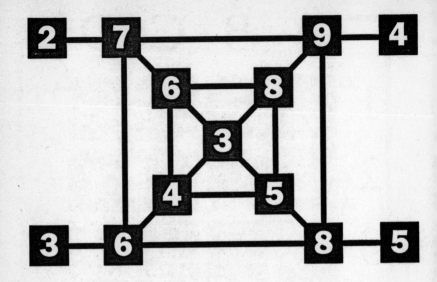

NUMBER PUZZLE 38

Start at the corner number and collect another
four numbers by following the paths shown.
Add the five numbers together.
How many times can you score 24?

ANSWER 28

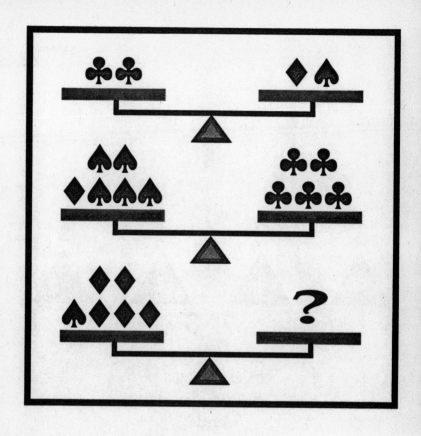

NUMBER PUZZLE 39

The top two scales are in perfect balance.
How many clubs will be needed to balance the
bottom set?

ANSWER 70

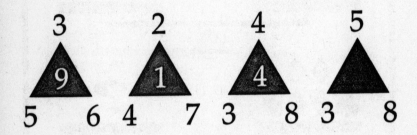

3
9
5   6

2
1
4   7

4
4
3   8

5

3   8

NUMBER PUZZLE 40

Which figure should be placed in the empty triangle?

ANSWER 18

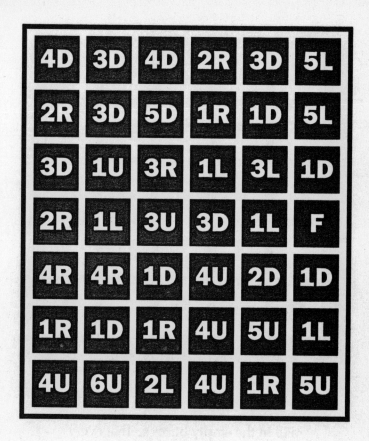

NUMBER PUZZLE 41

Here is an unusual safe. Each of the buttons must
be pressed once only in the correct order to open it.
The last button is always marked F. The number of
moves and the direction is marked on each button.
Thus 1U would mean one move up whilst 1L
would mean one move to the left.
Which button is the first you must press?

ANSWER 59

NUMBER PUZZLE 42

Fill in the empty boxes so that every
line adds up to the same, including the lines
that go from corner to corner. Which two
numbers will be used to do this?

ANSWER 267

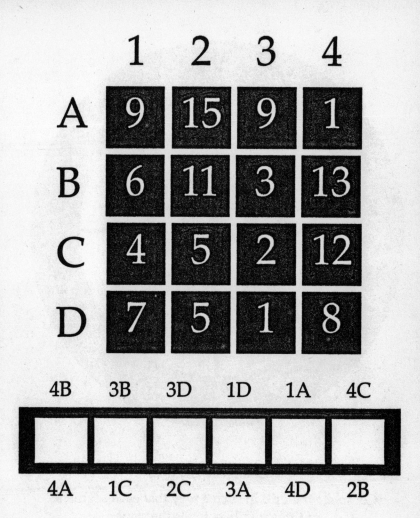

	1	2	3	4
A	9	15	9	1
B	6	11	3	13
C	4	5	2	12
D	7	5	1	8

4B	3B	3D	1D	1A	4C
4A	1C	2C	3A	4D	2B

NUMBER PUZZLE 43

Find the correct six numbers to put in the frame.
There are two choices for each square, for example
1A would give the number 9. When the correct
numbers have been found an easy series will
appear. What is the series?

ANSWER 229

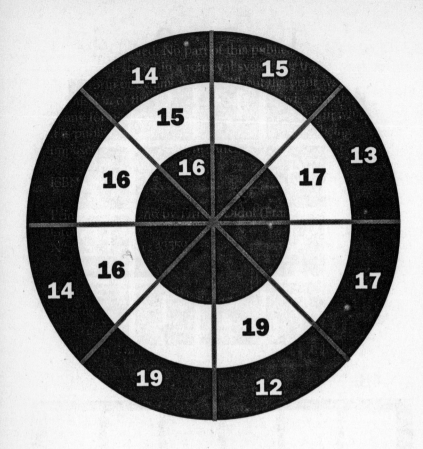

NUMBER PUZZLE 44

Complete the grid in such a way that each segment
of three numbers totals the same.
When this has been done correctly each of the three
concentric circles of eight numbers will produce
three identical totals.
Now complete the diagram.

ANSWER 7

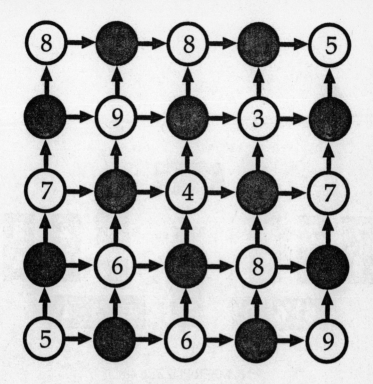

NUMBER PUZZLE 45

Move from the bottom left-hand corner to the top
right-hand corner following the arrows. Add the
numbers on your route together. If each black spot
is worth 2, how many different routes are there
to score 40?

ANSWER 100

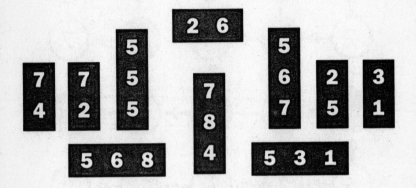

NUMBER PUZZLE 46

Place the tiles in a square to give some five-figure numbers. When this has been done accurately the same five numbers can be read both down and across. How does the finished square look?

ANSWER 48

NUMBER PUZZLE 47

Start in the middle circle and move from circle to
touching circle. Collect the four numbers which
will total 90. Once a route has been found return to
the middle circle and start again.
If a route can be found, which obeys the above
rules but follows both a clockwise and an
anticlockwise path, it is treated as two different
routes. How many different ways are there?

ANSWER 89

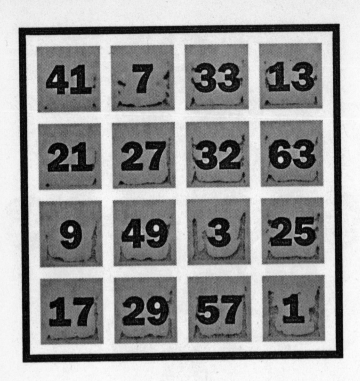

NUMBER PUZZLE 48

Which of the numbers in the square is the
odd one out and why?

ANSWER 206

NUMBER PUZZLE 49

Each slice of this cake has a number
written on it. Using the numbers shown how many
different ways are there to add three numbers
together to make a total of 13? A number can
be used more than once, but a group cannot
be repeated in a different order.

ANSWER 238

NUMBER PUZZLE 50

Which number should replace the question mark in the diagram?

ANSWER 37

NUMBER PUZZLE 51

You have four shots with each go to score 49.
Aim at this target and work out how many
different ways there are to make the score. Assume
each shot scores and once four numbers have been
used the same four cannot be used again in
another order. How many are there?

ANSWER 79

NUMBER PUZZLE 52

Fill up this square with the numbers 1 to 5
so that no row, column or diagonal line of five
squares uses the same number more than
once. What number should replace
the question mark?

ANSWER 278

PUZZLE 53

The numbers in the middle section
have some connection with those down the sides.
Find out what it is and tell us what should
replace the question mark?

ANSWER 210

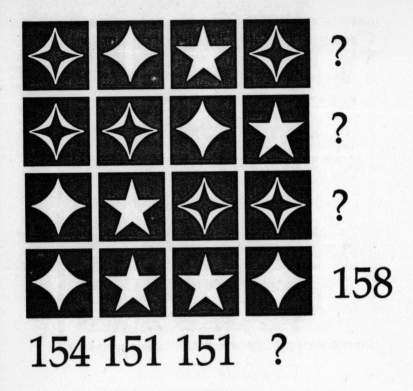

?

?

?

158

154 151 151 ?

NUMBER PUZZLE 54

The contents of each box has a value. The total of the values is shown alongside a row or beneath a column. Which number should replace the question marks?

ANSWER 27

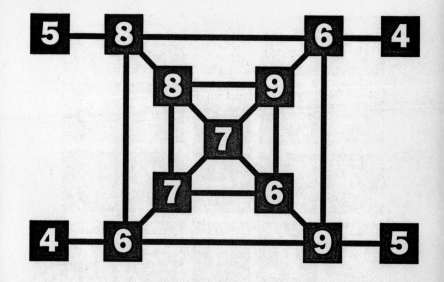

NUMBER PUZZLE 55

Start at the corner number and collect another four
numbers by following the paths shown. Add the
five numbers together.
What is the lowest number you can score?

ANSWER 69

NUMBER PUZZLE 56

Move from square to adjacent square either
vertically or horizontally. Begin at the bottom
left-hand square and end at the top right-hand
square. Collect nine numbers and total them.
How many different ways are there to total 35?

ANSWER 17

A B C D E

A	B	C	D	E
6	1	5	7	
5	1	4	6	
4	2	2	6	4
3	2	1	5	4
4	1	3	5	

NUMBER PUZZLE 57

There is a relationship between the columns of
numbers in this diagram. The letters above the grid
are there to help you. Which number should be
placed in the empty squares?

ANSWER 58

NUMBER PUZZLE 58

Move up or across from the bottom left-hand 2 to
the top right-hand 3. Collect nine numbers and add
them together. What is the highest you can score?

ANSWER 254

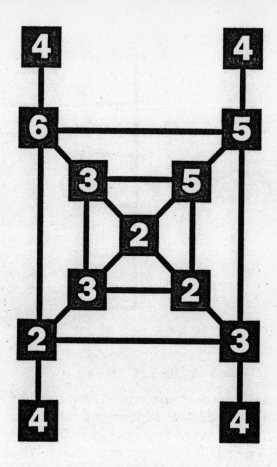

NUMBER PUZZLE 59

Start at any corner and follow the lines. Add up the
first four numbers you meet and then add on the
corner number. What is the highest you can score?

ANSWER 208

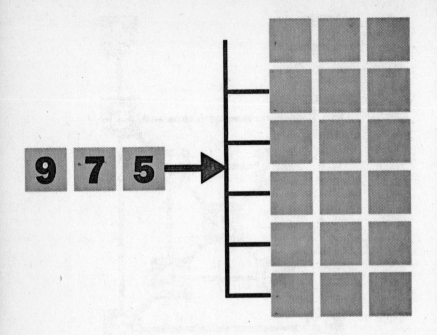

NUMBER PUZZLE 60

Place six three digit numbers of 100 plus at the end of 975 so that six numbers of six digits are produced. When each number is divided by 65.5 six whole numbers can be found. Which numbers should be placed in the grid?

ANSWER 6

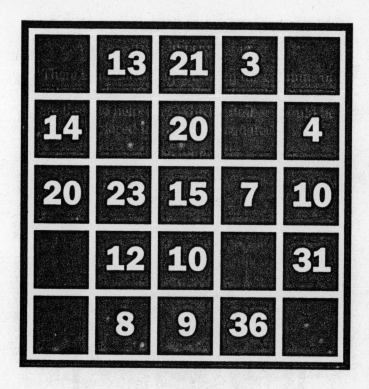

NUMBER PUZZLE 61

Each row, column and five-figure diagonal line
in this diagram must total 75. Three different
numbers must be used, as many times as necessary,
to achieve this.
What are the numbers?

ANSWER 99

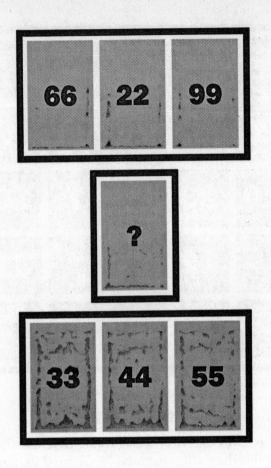

NUMBER PUZZLE 62

Place in the middle box a number larger than 1.
If the number is the correct one, all the other
numbers can be divided by it without leaving any
remainder. What is the number?

ANSWER 240

NUMBER PUZZLE 63

Each sector of the circle follows a pattern.
What number should replace the question mark?

ANSWER 217

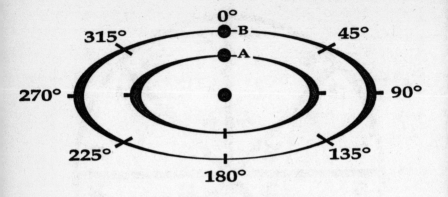

NUMBER PUZZLE 64

Two planets are in line with each other and the sun. The outer planet will orbit the sun every six years. The inner planet takes two years. Both move in a clockwise direction. When will they next form a straight line with each other and the sun? The diagram should help you.

ANSWER 47

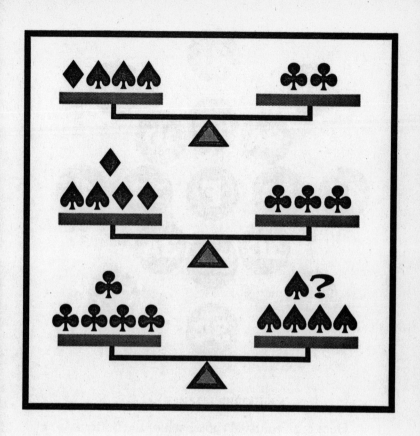

NUMBER PUZZLE 65

The top two scales are in perfect balance.
How many diamonds will be needed to balance the
bottom set?

ANSWER 88

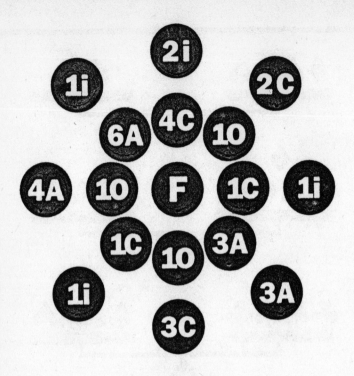

NUMBER PUZZLE 66

Here is an unusual safe. Each of the buttons
must be pressed only once in the correct order to
open it. The last button is marked F. The number of
moves and the direction is marked on each button.
Thus 1i would mean one move in, whilst 1O would
mean one move out. 1C would mean one move
clockwise and 1A would mean one move
anti-clockwise. Which button is the first
you must press? Here's a clue:
look around the outer rim.

ANSWER 220

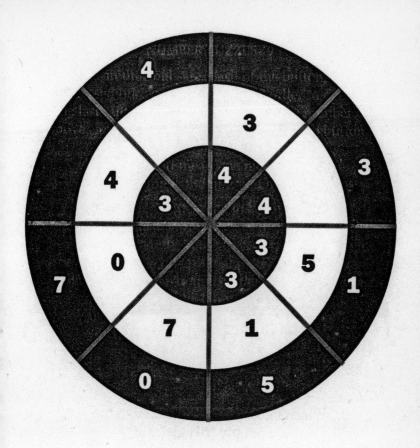

NUMBER PUZZLE 67

Each slice of this cake adds up to the
same number. Also each ring of the cake totals
the same. Which number should
appear in the blanks?

ANSWER 205

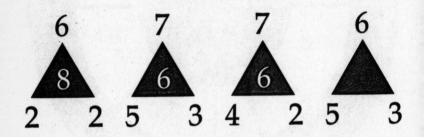

6
8
2   2

7
6
5   3

7
6
4   2

6
5   3

NUMBER PUZZLE 68

Which figure should be placed in the
empty triangle?

ANSWER 36

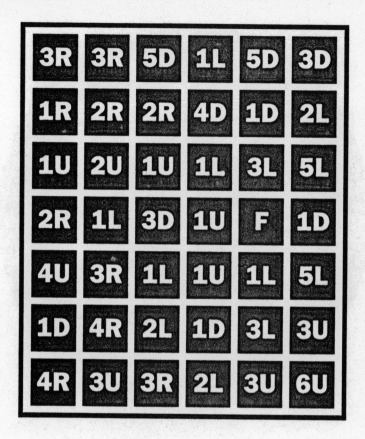

3R	3R	5D	1L	5D	3D
1R	2R	2R	4D	1D	2L
1U	2U	1U	1L	3L	5L
2R	1L	3D	1U	F	1D
4U	3R	1L	1U	1L	5L
1D	4R	2L	1D	3L	3U
4R	3U	3R	2L	3U	6U

NUMBER PUZZLE 69

Here is an unusual safe. Each of the buttons bar
one must be pressed once only in the correct order
to open it. The last button is always marked F.
The number of moves and the direction is marked
on each button. Thus 1U would mean one move up
whilst 1L would mean one move to the left.
Which button is the first you must press?

ANSWER 78

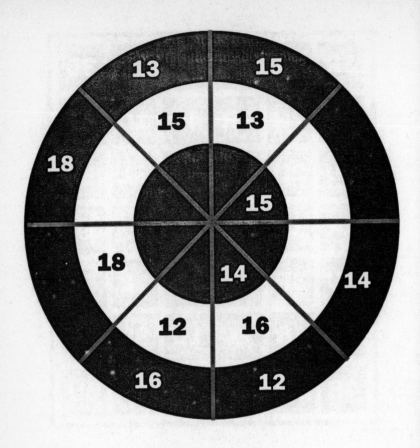

NUMBER PUZZLE 70

Complete the grid in such a way that each segment
of three numbers totals the same.
When this has been done correctly each of the three
concentric circles of eight numbers will produce
identical totals.
Now complete the diagram.

ANSWER 26

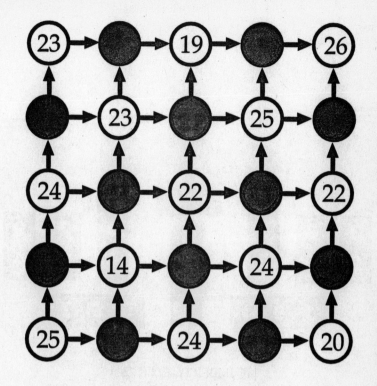

NUMBER PUZZLE 71

Move from the bottom left-hand corner to the top right-hand corner following the arrows. Add the numbers on your route together. If each black spot is worth minus 13, how many different routes are there to score 69?

ANSWER 68

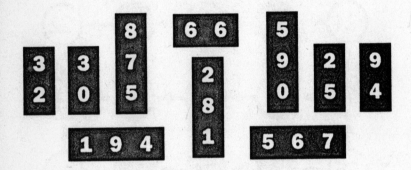

NUMBER PUZZLE 72

Place the tiles in a square to give some five-figure numbers. When this has been done accurately the same five numbers can be read both down and across. How does the finished square look?

ANSWER 16

NUMBER PUZZLE 73

Start in the middle circle and move from circle to touching circle. Collect the four numbers which will total 42. Once a route has been found return to the middle circle and start again.

If a route can be found, which obeys the above rules but follows both a clockwise and an anticlockwise path, it is treated as two different routes. How many different ways are there?

ANSWER 57

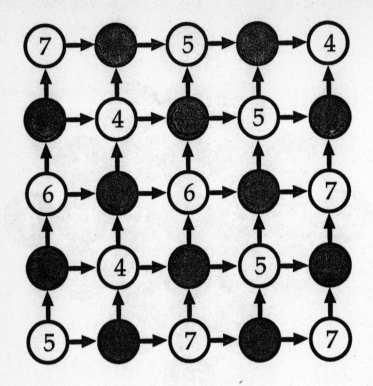

NUMBER PUZZLE 74

Move from the bottom left-hand 5 to the top
right-hand 4 adding together all five numbers.
Each black circle is worth minus 3 and this should
be taken away from your total each time you meet
one. What is the highest total you can find?

ANSWER 255

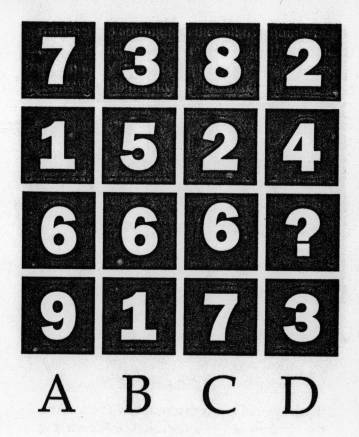

NUMBER PUZZLE 75

The numbers in column D are linked in
some way to those in A, B and C. What number
should replace the question mark?

ANSWER 274

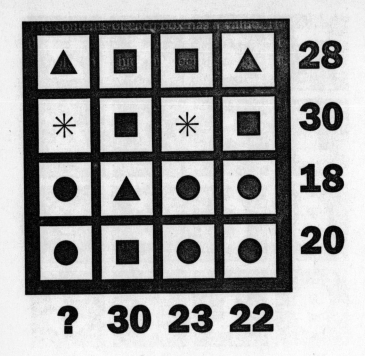

PUZZLE 76

Each symbol is worth a number. The total of
the symbols can be found alongside each row
and column. What number should replace
the question mark?

ANSWER 227

NUMBER PUZZLE 77

Start at the middle 7 and move from circle to touching circle. Collect three numbers and add them to the 7. How many different routes are there to make a total of 20?

ANSWER 276

NUMBER PUZZLE 78

Which number should replace the question marks
in the diagram?

ANSWER 5

NUMBER PUZZLE 79

You have four shots with each go to score 48. Aim
at this target and work out how many different
ways there are to make the score. Assume each
shot scores and once four numbers have been used
the same four cannot be used again in another
order. How many are there?

ANSWER 98

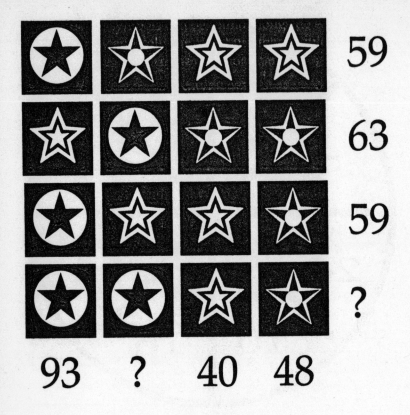

59

63

59

?

93   ?   40   48

NUMBER PUZZLE 80

The contents of each box has a value. The total of the values is shown alongside a row or beneath a column. Which number should replace the question marks?

ANSWER 46

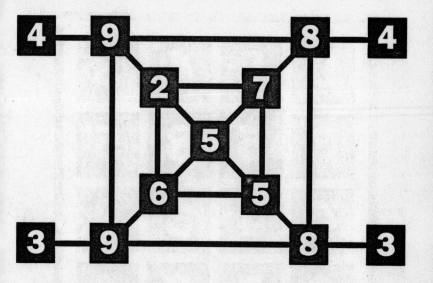

NUMBER PUZZLE 81

Start at any corner number and collect another four
numbers by following the paths shown. Add the
five numbers together.
How many times can you score 29?

ANSWER 87

NUMBER PUZZLE 82

Divide up the box into four identical shapes.
The numbers in each shape add up to the same.
How is this done?

ANSWER 207

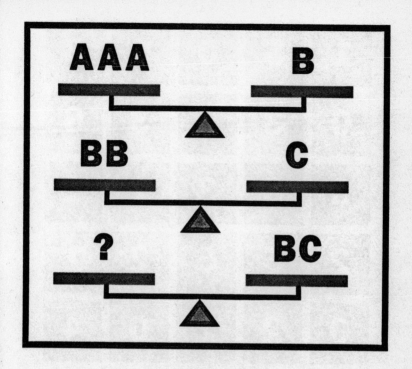

NUMBER PUZZLE 83

Scales 1 and 2 are in perfect balance. If one C is the same as four As, how many As are needed to balance the third set?

ANSWER 262

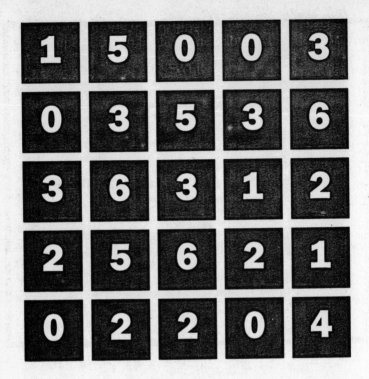

NUMBER PUZZLE 84

Move from square to adjacent square either
vertically or horizontally. Begin at the bottom
left-hand square and end at the top right-hand
square. Collect nine numbers and total them.
How many different ways are there to total 30?

ANSWER 35

A B C D E

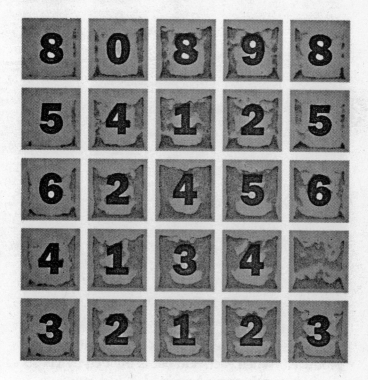

NUMBER PUZZLE 85

There is a relationship between the columns of numbers in this diagram. The letters above the grid are there to help you. Which number should be placed in the empty squares?

ANSWER 77

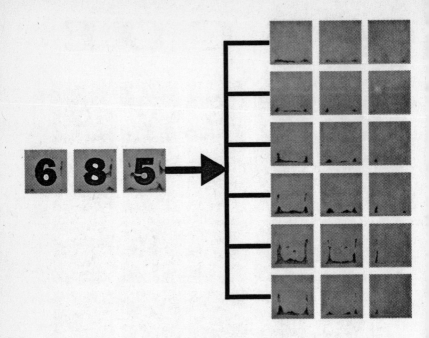

NUMBER PUZZLE 86

Place six three digit numbers of 100 plus at the end
of 685 so that six numbers of six digits are
produced. When each number is divided by 111 six
whole numbers can be found. Which numbers
should be placed in the grid?

ANSWER 25

NUMBER PUZZLE 87

Each row, column and five-figure diagonal line
in this diagram must total 70. Three different
numbers must be used, as many times as necessary,
to achieve this.
What are the numbers?

ANSWER 67

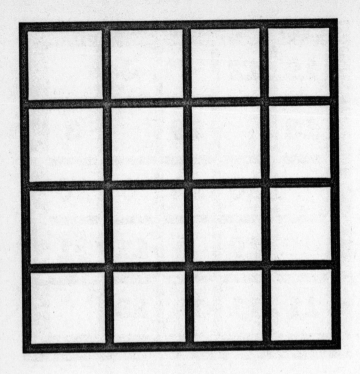

NUMBER PUZZLE 88

How many rectangles of any size can
you find in this diagram?

ANSWER 233

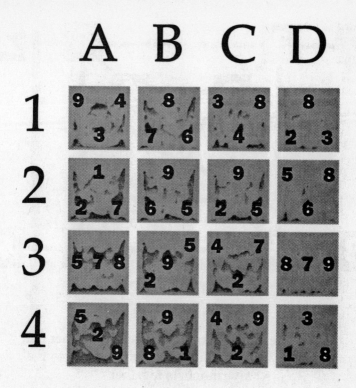

NUMBER PUZZLE 89

Which squares contain the same numbers?

ANSWER 224

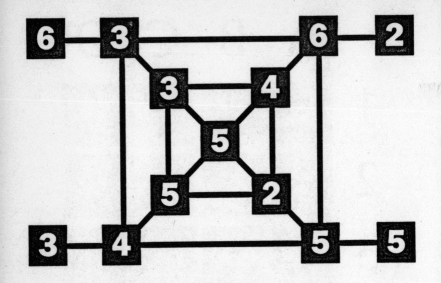

NUMBER PUZZLE 90

Start at the corner number and collect another four
numbers by following the paths shown. Add the
five numbers together.
How many times can you score 17?

ANSWER 15

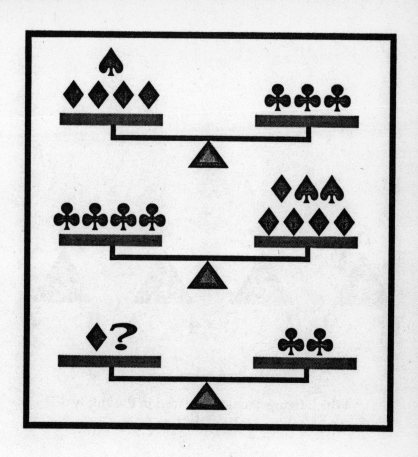

NUMBER PUZZLE 91

The top two scales are in perfect balance.
How many spades will be needed to balance the
bottom set?

ANSWER 56

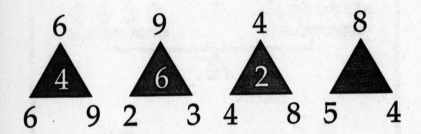

NUMBER PUZZLE 92

Which figure should be placed in the empty triangle?

ANSWER 4

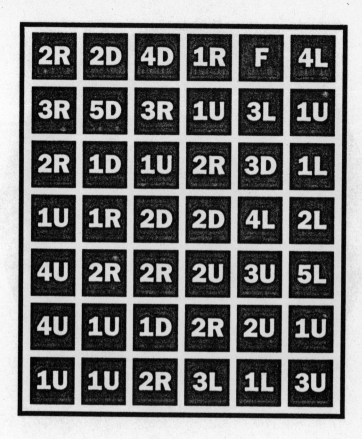

2R	2D	4D	1R	F	4L
3R	5D	3R	1U	3L	1U
2R	1D	1U	2R	3D	1L
1U	1R	2D	2D	4L	2L
4U	2R	2R	2U	3U	5L
4U	1U	1D	2R	2U	1U
1U	1U	2R	3L	1L	3U

NUMBER PUZZLE 93

Here is an unusual safe. Each of the buttons must
be pressed once only in the correct order to open it.
The last button is always marked F. The number of
moves and the direction is marked on each button.
Thus 1U would mean one move up
whilst 1L would mean one move to the left.
Which button is the first you must press?

ANSWER 97

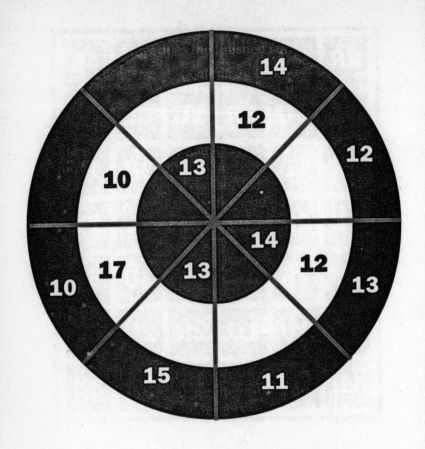

NUMBER PUZZLE 94

Complete the grid in such a way that each segment
of three numbers totals the same.
When this has been done correctly each of the three
concentric circles of eight numbers will produce
identical totals.
Now complete the diagram.

ANSWER 45

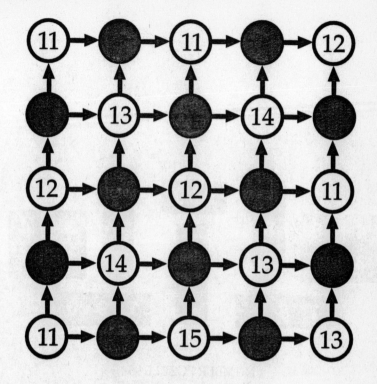

NUMBER PUZZLE 95

Move from the bottom left-hand corner to the top right-hand corner following the arrows. Add the numbers on your route together. If each black spot is worth 9, how many different routes are there to score 94?

ANSWER 86

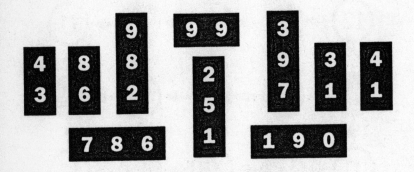

NUMBER PUZZLE 96

Place the tiles in a square to give some five-figure
numbers. When this has been done accurately the
same five numbers can be read both downwards
and across. How does the finished square look?

ANSWER 34

NUMBER PUZZLE 97

Start in the middle circle and move from circle to touching circle. Collect the four numbers which will total 15. Once a route has been found return to the middle circle and start again.

If a route can be found, which obeys the above rules but follows both a clockwise and an anticlockwise path, it is treated as two different routes. How many different ways are there?

ANSWER 76

NUMBER PUZZLE 98

Fill in the empty boxes so that every line
adds up to 20. What number should replace
the question mark?

ANSWER 277

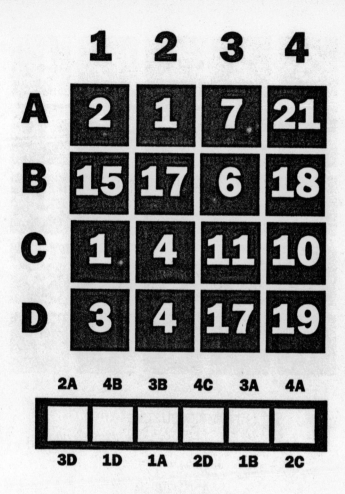

	1	2	3	4
A	2	1	7	21
B	15	17	6	18
C	1	4	11	10
D	3	4	17	19

2A	4B	3B	4C	3A	4A
3D	1D	1A	2D	1B	2C

NUMBER PUZZLE 99

Find the correct six numbers to put in the frame.
There are two choices for each square, for example
1A would give the number 2. When the correct
numbers have been found an easy series will
appear. What is the series?

ANSWER 212

NUMBER PUZZLE 100

Which number should replace the question marks
in the diagram?

ANSWER 24

NUMBER PUZZLE 101

You have three shots with each go to score 26. Aim
at this target and work out how many different
ways there are to make the score. Assume each
shot scores and once three numbers have been used
the same three cannot be used again in another
order. How many are there?

ANSWER 66

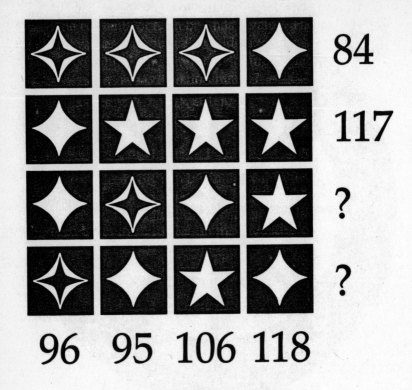

84

117

?

?

96 95 106 118

NUMBER PUZZLE 102

The contents of each box has a value. The total of the values is shown alongside a row or beneath a column. Which number should replace the question marks?

ANSWER 14

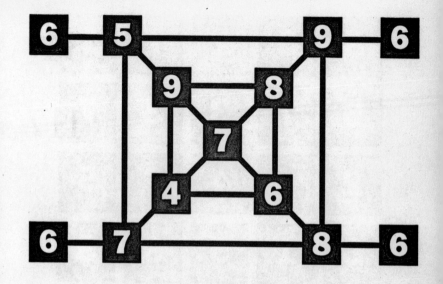

NUMBER PUZZLE 103

Start at any corner number and collect another four
numbers by following the paths shown. Add the
five numbers together.
What is the highest number you can score?

ANSWER 55

NUMBER PUZZLE 104

Move from square to adjacent square either
vertically or horizontally. Begin at the bottom
left-hand square and end at the top right-hand
square. Collect nine numbers and total them.
What is the lowest possible score?

ANSWER 3

A B C D E

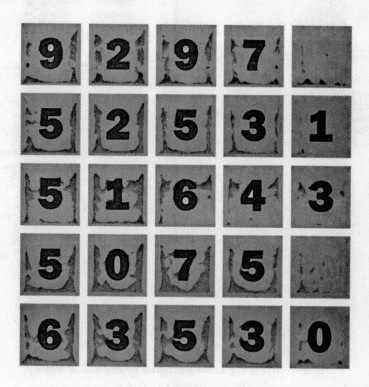

A	B	C	D	E
9	2	9	7	
5	2	5	3	1
5	1	6	4	3
5	0	7	5	
6	3	5	3	0

NUMBER PUZZLE 105

There is a relationship between the columns of
numbers in this diagram. The letters above the grid
are there to help you. Which number should be
placed in the empty squares?

ANSWER 96

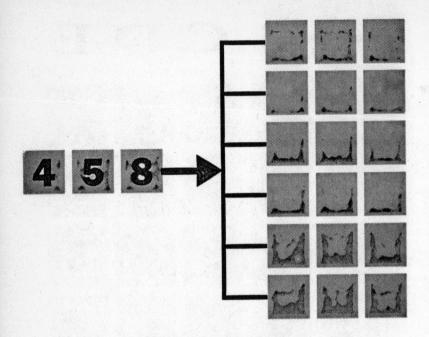

NUMBER PUZZLE 106

Place six three digit numbers of 100 plus at the end
of 458 so that six numbers of six digits are
produced. When each number is divided by 122 six
whole numbers can be found. Which numbers
should be placed in the grid?

ANSWER 44

NUMBER PUZZLE 107

Each row, column and five-figure diagonal line
in this diagram must total 65. Two different
numbers must be used, as many times as necessary,
to achieve this.
What are the numbers?

ANSWER 85

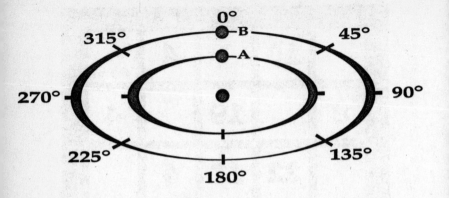

NUMBER PUZZLE 108

Two planets are in line with each other and the
sun. The outer planet will orbit the sun every
fifteen years. The inner planet takes five years.
Both move in a clockwise direction. When will they
next form a straight line with each other and the
sun? The diagram should help you.

ANSWER 33

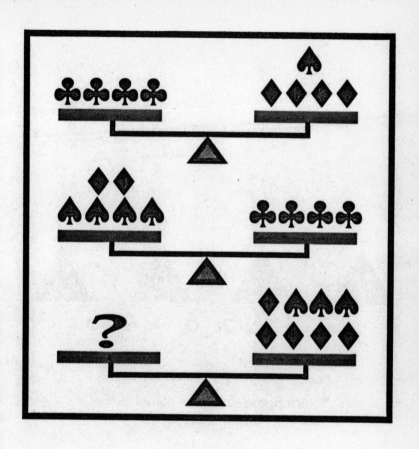

NUMBER PUZZLE 109

The top two scales are in perfect balance.
How many clubs will be needed to balance the
bottom set?

ANSWER 75

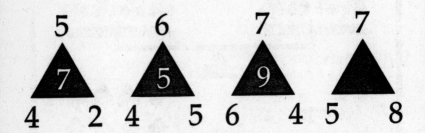

5   6   7   7

7   5   9

4   2   4   5   6   4   5   8

NUMBER PUZZLE 110

Which figure should be placed in the
empty triangle?

ANSWER 23

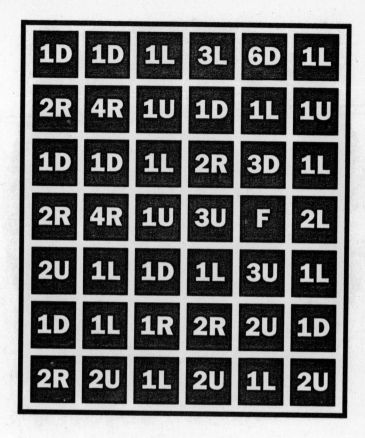

1D	1D	1L	3L	6D	1L
2R	4R	1U	1D	1L	1U
1D	1D	1L	2R	3D	1L
2R	4R	1U	3U	F	2L
2U	1L	1D	1L	3U	1L
1D	1L	1R	2R	2U	1D
2R	2U	1L	2U	1L	2U

NUMBER PUZZLE 111

Here is an unusual safe. Each of the buttons must
be pressed once only in the correct order to open it.
The last button is always marked F. The number of
moves and the direction is marked on each button.
Thus 1U would mean one move up
whilst 1L would mean one move to the left.
Which button is the first you must press?

ANSWER 65

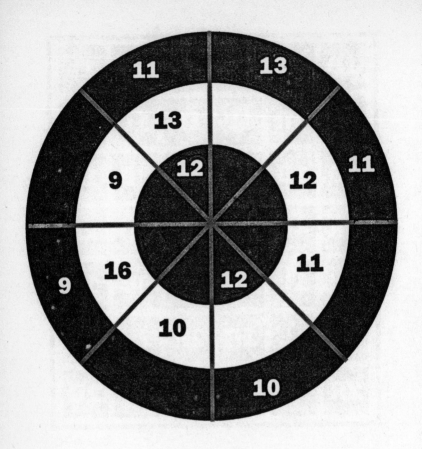

NUMBER PUZZLE 112

Complete the grid in such a way that each segment
of three numbers totals the same.
When this has been done correctly each of the three
concentric circles of eight numbers will produce
identical totals.
Now complete the diagram.

ANSWER 13

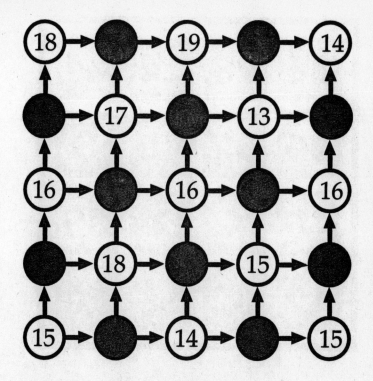

NUMBER PUZZLE 113

Move from the bottom left-hand corner to the top right-hand corner following the arrows. Add the numbers on your route together. If each black spot is worth minus 7, how many different routes are there to score 51?

ANSWER 54

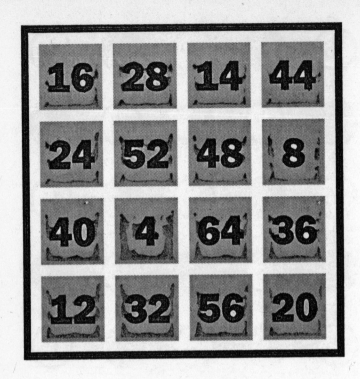

NUMBER PUZZLE 114

Which of the numbers in the square is the
odd one out and why?

ANSWER 230

NUMBER PUZZLE 115

Fill up this square with the numbers
1 to 5 so that no row, column or diagonal line of
five squares uses the same number more than once.
What number should replace the question mark?

ANSWER 204

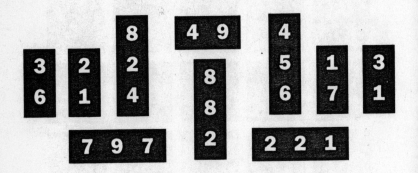

NUMBER PUZZLE 116

Place the tiles in the square to give some five-figure numbers. When this has been done accurately the same five numbers can be read both down and across. How does the finished square look?

ANSWER 2

NUMBER PUZZLE 117

Start in the middle circle and move from circle to touching circle. Collect the four numbers which will total 100. Once a route has been found return to the middle circle and start again.

If a route can be found, which obeys the above rules but follows both a clockwise and an anticlockwise path, it is treated as two different routes. How many different ways are there?

ANSWER 95

NUMBER PUZZLE 118

Which number should replace the question mark in
the diagram?

ANSWER 43

NUMBER PUZZLE 119

You have three shots with each go to score 42. Aim at this target and work out how many different ways there are to make the score. Assume each shot scores and once three numbers have been used the same three cannot be used again in another order. How many are there?

ANSWER 84

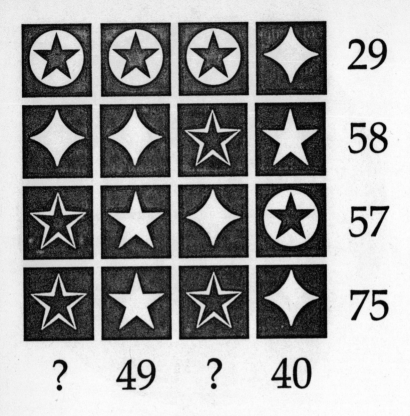

29

58

57

75

? 49 ? 40

NUMBER PUZZLE 120

The contents of each box has a value. The total of the values is shown alongside a row or beneath a column. Which number should replace the question mark?

ANSWER 32

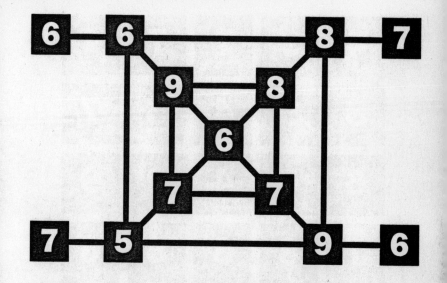

NUMBER PUZZLE 121

Start at any corner number and collect another four
numbers by following the paths shown. Add the
five numbers together.
What is the highest number you can score
and how many times can you score it?

ANSWER 74

NUMBER PUZZLE 122

Move from square to adjacent square either
vertically or horizontally. Begin at the bottom
left-hand square and end at the top right-hand
square. Collect nine numbers and total them.
How many times can you score 60?

ANSWER 22

A B C D E

NUMBER PUZZLE 123

There is a relationship between the columns of numbers in this diagram. The letters above the grid are there to help you.
Which number should be placed in the empty squares?

ANSWER 64

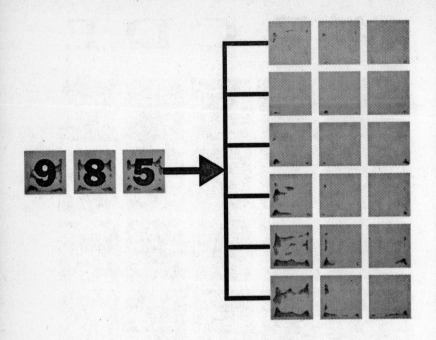

NUMBER PUZZLE 124

Place six three digit numbers of 100 plus at the end of 985 so that six numbers of six digits are produced. When each number is divided by 133 six whole numbers can be found. Which numbers should be placed in the grid?

ANSWER 12

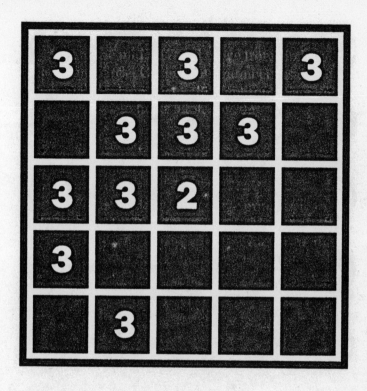

NUMBER PUZZLE 125

Each row, column and five-figure diagonal line
in this diagram must total 10. Three different
numbers must be used, as many times as necessary,
to achieve this.
What are the numbers?

ANSWER 53

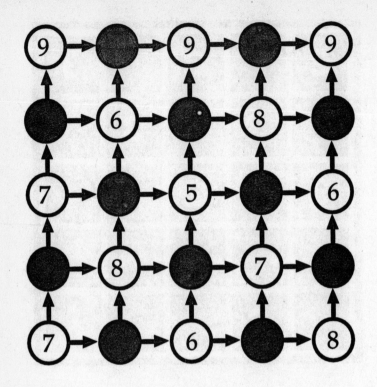

NUMBER PUZZLE 126

Move from the bottom left-hand corner to the top right-hand corner following the arrows. Add the numbers on your route together. If each black spot is worth minus 4, what is the lowest number you can score?

ANSWER 1

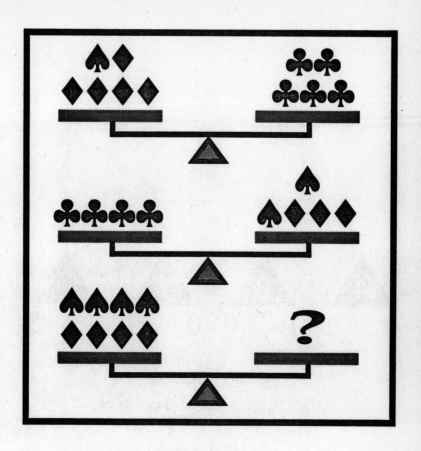

NUMBER PUZZLE 127

The top two scales are in perfect balance.
How many clubs will be needed to balance the
bottom set?

ANSWER 42

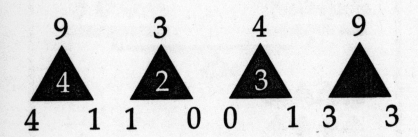

NUMBER PUZZLE 128

Which figure should be placed in the
empty triangle?

ANSWER 94

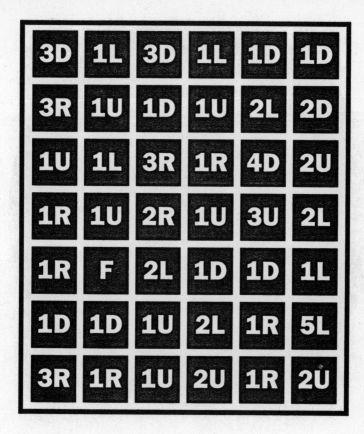

NUMBER PUZZLE 129

Here is an unusual safe. Each of the buttons must
be pressed once only in the correct order to open it.
The last button is always marked F. The number of
moves and the direction is marked on each button.
Thus 1U would mean one move upwards
whilst 1L would mean one move to the left.
Which button is the first you must press?

ANSWER 83

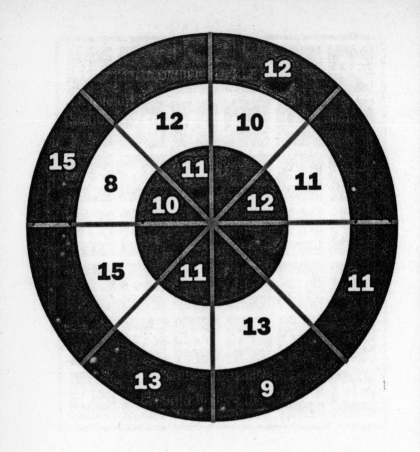

NUMBER PUZZLE 130

Complete the grid in such a way that each segment
of three numbers totals the same.
When this has been done correctly each of the three
concentric circles of eight numbers will produce
three identical totals.
Now complete the diagram.

ANSWER 31

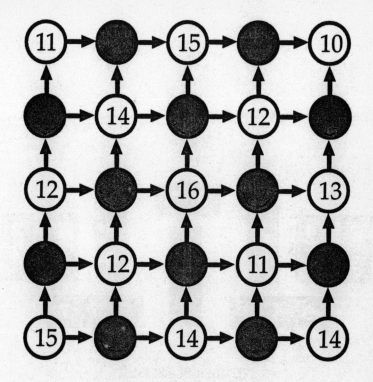

NUMBER PUZZLE 131

Move from the bottom left-hand corner to the top right-hand corner following the arrows. Add the numbers on your route together. If each black spot is worth minus 3, which number can be scored only once?

ANSWER 73

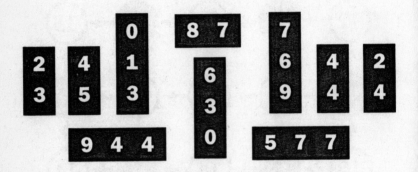

NUMBER PUZZLE 132

Place the tiles in a square to give some five-figure numbers. When this has been done accurately the same five numbers can be read both down and across. How does the finished square look?

ANSWER 21

NUMBER PUZZLE 133

Start in the middle circle and move from circle to
touching circle. Collect the four numbers which
will total 30. Once a route has been found return to
the middle circle and start again.
If a route can be found, which obeys the above
rules but follows both a clockwise and an
anticlockwise path, it is treated as two different
routes. How many different ways are there?

ANSWER 63

NUMBER PUZZLE 134

Each slice of this cake has a number written on it. Using the numbers shown how many different ways are there to add four numbers together to make a total of 12? A number can be used more than once, but a group cannot be repeated in a different order.

ANSWER 244

NUMBER PUZZLE 135

Look at the pattern of numbers in the diagram.
What number should replace the question mark?

ANSWER 260

NUMBER PUZZLE 136

Which number should replace the question marks in the diagram?

ANSWER 11

NUMBER PUZZLE 137

You have four shots with each go to score 62. Aim
at this target and work out how many different
ways there are to make the score. Assume each
shot scores and once four numbers have been used
the same four cannot be used again in another
order. How many are there?

ANSWER 52

156

179

113

158

135   ?   ?   ?

NUMBER PUZZLE 138

The contents of each box has a value. The total of the values is shown alongside a row or beneath a column. Which number should replace the question mark?

ANSWER 104

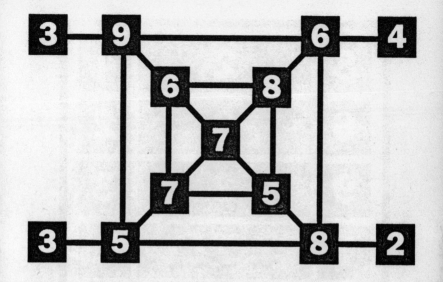

NUMBER PUZZLE 139

Start at the corner number and collect another four
numbers by following the paths shown. Add the
five numbers together. What is the lowest number
you can score and how many times can you
score it?

ANSWER 93

NUMBER PUZZLE 140

The numbers in the middle section have
some connection with those down the sides.
Find out what it is and tell us what should
replace the question mark?

ANSWER 251

NUMBER PUZZLE 141

Move up or across from the bottom left-hand 2 to
the top right-hand 3.Collect nine numbers and add
them together. What is the highest you can score?

ANSWER 226

NUMBER PUZZLE 142

Move from square to adjacent square either
vertically or horizontally. Begin at the bottom
left-hand square and end at the top right-hand
square. Collect nine numbers and total them.
How many different ways are there to total 31?

ANSWER 41

A B C D E

NUMBER PUZZLE 143

There is a relationship between the columns of
numbers in this diagram. The letters above the grid
are there to help you. Which number should be
placed in the empty squares?

ANSWER 167

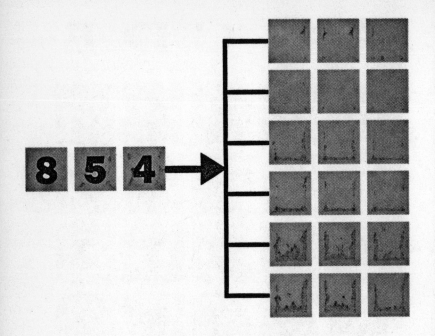

NUMBER PUZZLE 144

Place six three digit numbers of 100 plus at the end
of 854 so that six numbers of six digits are
produced. When each number is divided by 149 six
whole numbers can be found. Which numbers
should be placed in the grid?

ANSWER 115

NUMBER PUZZLE 145

Each row, column and five-figure diagonal line
in this diagram must total 15. Three different
numbers must be used, as many times as necessary,
to achieve this.
What are the numbers?

ANSWER 187

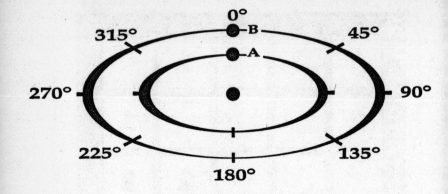

NUMBER PUZZLE 146

Two planets are in line with each other and the
sun. The outer planet will orbit the sun every one
hundred years. The inner planet takes twenty
years. Both move in a clockwise direction. When
will they next form a straight line with each other
and the sun? The diagram should help you.

ANSWER 156

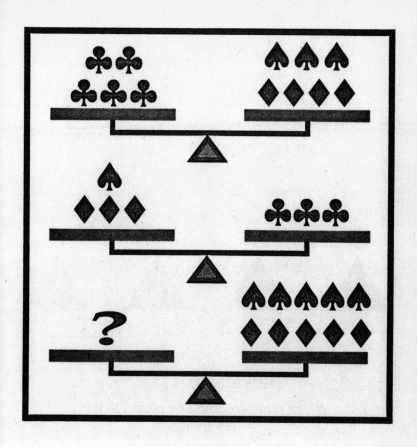

NUMBER PUZZLE 147

The top two scales are in perfect balance.
How many clubs will be needed to balance the
bottom set?

ANSWER 197

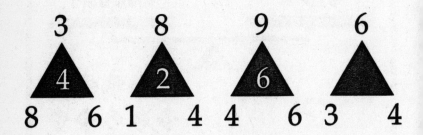

NUMBER PUZZLE 148

Which number should be placed in the empty triangle?

ANSWER 145

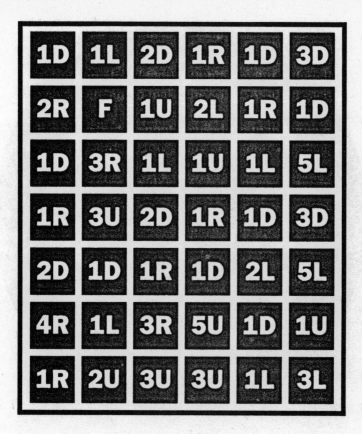

1D	1L	2D	1R	1D	3D
2R	F	1U	2L	1R	1D
1D	3R	1L	1U	1L	5L
1R	3U	2D	1R	1D	3D
2D	1D	1R	1D	2L	5L
4R	1L	3R	5U	1D	1U
1R	2U	3U	3U	1L	3L

NUMBER PUZZLE 149

Here is an unusual safe. Each of the buttons must
be pressed once only in the correct order to open it.
The last button is always marked F. The number of
moves and the direction is marked on each button.
Thus 1U would mean one move up
whilst 1L would mean one move to the left.
Which button is the first you must press?

ANSWER 166

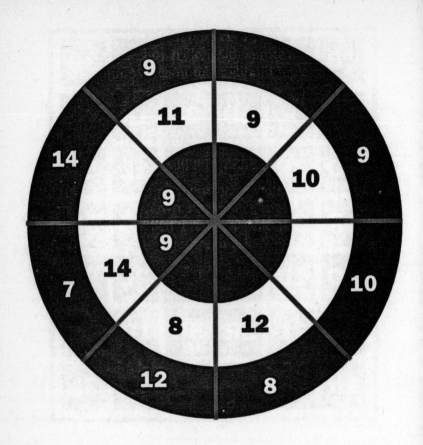

NUMBER PUZZLE 150

Complete the grid in such a way that each segment
of three numbers totals the same.
When this has been done correctly each of the three
concentric circles of eight numbers will produce
identical totals. Now complete the diagram.

ANSWER 114

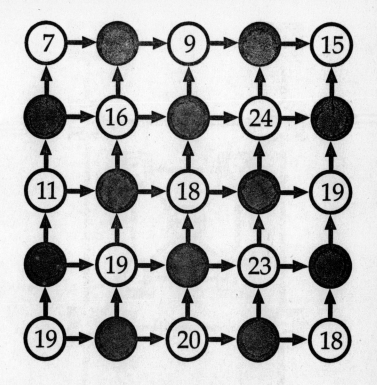

NUMBER PUZZLE 151

Move from the bottom left-hand corner to the top right-hand corner following the arrows. Add the numbers on your route together. If each black spot is worth minus 17, how many different routes are there to score 2?

ANSWER 135

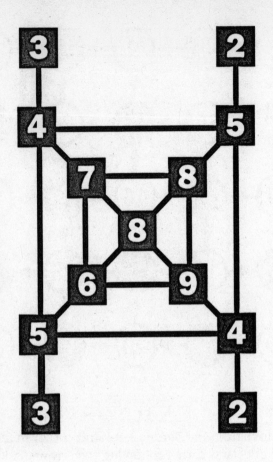

NUMBER PUZZLE 152

Start at any corner and follow the lines.
Add up the first four numbers you meet and then
add on the corner number. How many different
routes will add up to 21?

ANSWER 273

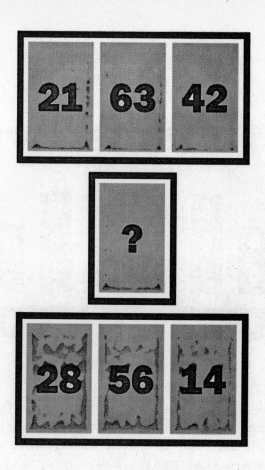

NUMBER PUZZLE 153

Place in the middle box a number larger than 1.
If the number is the correct one, all the other
numbers can be divided by it without leaving any
remainder. What is the number?

ANSWER 243

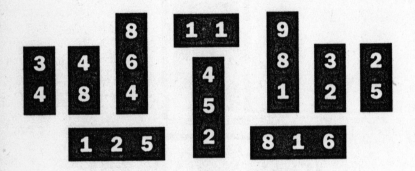

NUMBER PUZZLE 154

Place the tiles in a square to give some five-figure numbers. When this has been done accurately the same five numbers can be read both down and across. How does the finished square look?

ANSWER 155

NUMBER PUZZLE 155

Start in the middle circle and move from circle to
touching circle. Collect the four numbers which
will total 10. Once a route has been found return to
the middle circle and start again.
If a route can be found, which obeys the above
rules but follows both a clockwise and an
anticlockwise path, it is treated as two different
routes. How many different ways are there?

ANSWER 196

NUMBER PUZZLE 156

Which number should replace the question marks
in the diagram?

ANSWER 144

NUMBER PUZZLE 157

You have five shots with each go to score 22. Aim
at this target and work out how many different
ways there are to make the score. Assume each
shot scores and once five numbers have been used
the same five cannot be used again in another
order. How many are there?

ANSWER 186

NUMBER PUZZLE 158

How many ways are there to score 25 on this
dartboard using four darts only? Each dart always
lands in a segment and no dart falls to the floor.
Once a group of numbers has been used it cannot
be repeated in a different order.

ANSWER 239

NUMBER PUZZLE 159

Fill in the empty boxes so that every line
adds up to 30. Use two numbers only, one of which
is double the other. What number should replace
the question mark?

ANSWER 259

NUMBER PUZZLE 160

The contents of each box has a value. The total of
the values is shown alongside a row or beneath a
column. Which number should replace the
question marks?

ANSWER 134

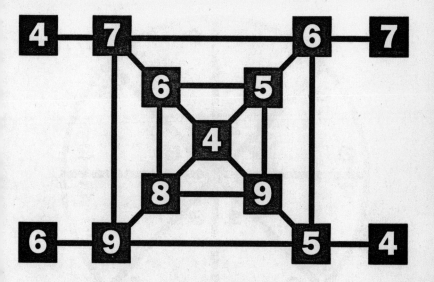

NUMBER PUZZLE 161

Start at any corner number and collect another four
numbers by following the paths shown. Add the
five numbers together.
How many times can you score 37?

ANSWER 176

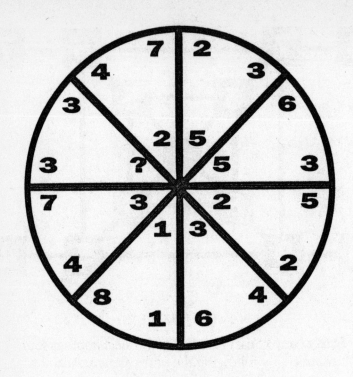

NUMBER PUZZLE 162

Each sector of the circle follows a pattern.
What number should replace the question mark?

ANSWER 232

NUMBER PUZZLE 163

Here is an unusual safe. Each of the buttons must be pressed only once in the correct order to open it. The last button is marked F. The number of moves and the direction is marked on each button. Thus 1i would mean one move in, whilst 1O would mean one move out. 1C would mean one move clockwise and 1A would mean one move anti-clockwise. Which button is the first you must press? Here's a clue: look on the inner circle.

ANSWER 275

NUMBER PUZZLE 164

Move from square to adjacent square either vertically or horizontally. Begin at the bottom left-hand square and end at the top right-hand square. Collect nine numbers and total them. How many different ways are there to total 46?

ANSWER 124

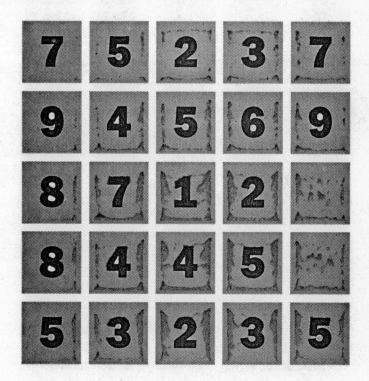

NUMBER PUZZLE 165

There is a relationship between the columns of numbers in this diagram. The letters above the grid are there to help you. Which number should be placed in the empty squares?

ANSWER 165

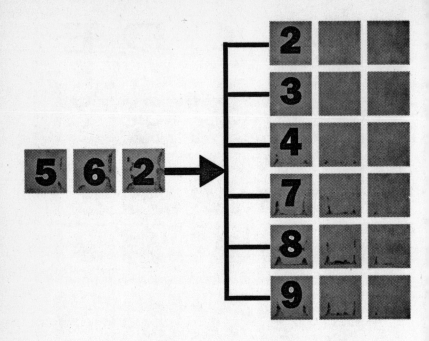

NUMBER PUZZLE 166

Place six three digit numbers of 100 plus at the end of 562 so that six numbers of six digits are produced. When each number is divided by 61.5 six whole numbers can be found. In this case, the first numbers are given. Which numbers should be placed in the grid?

ANSWER 113

NUMBER PUZZLE 167

Each row, column and five-figure diagonal line
in this diagram must total 20. Three different
numbers must be used, as many times as necessary,
to achieve this.
What are the numbers?

ANSWER 125

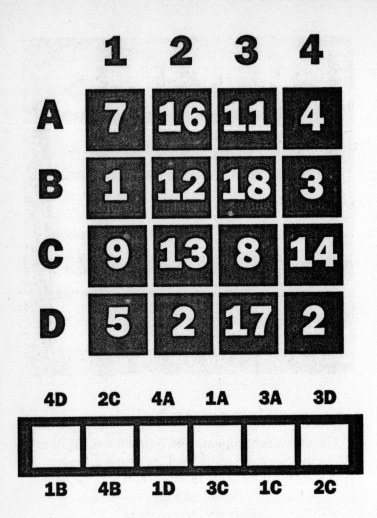

	1	2	3	4
A	7	16	11	4
B	1	12	18	3
C	9	13	8	14
D	5	2	17	2

4D	2C	4A	1A	3A	3D
1B	4B	1D	3C	1C	2C

NUMBER PUZZLE 168

Find the correct six numbers to put in the frame.
There are two choices for each square, for example
1A would give the number 7. When the correct
numbers have been found an easy series will
appear. What is the series?

ANSWER 231

NUMBER PUZZLE 169

Which two numbers on the square do not
fit the pattern and why?

ANSWER 237

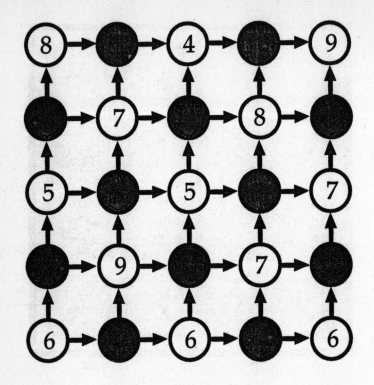

NUMBER PUZZLE 170

Move from the bottom left-hand corner to the top right-hand corner following the arrows. Add the numbers on your route together. If each black spot is worth minus 3, how many different ways can you score 20?

ANSWER 154

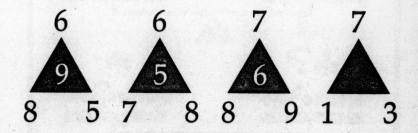

NUMBER PUZZLE 171

Which figure should be placed in the
empty triangle?

ANSWER 143

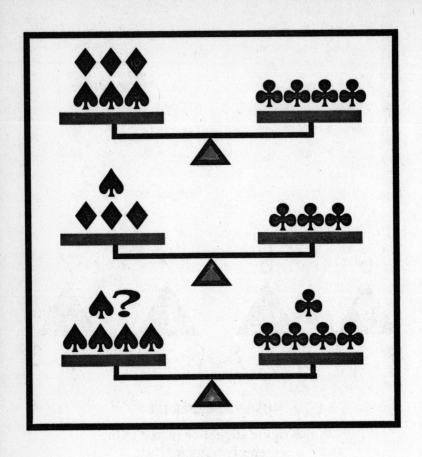

NUMBER PUZZLE 172

The top two scales are in perfect balance.
How many diamonds will be needed to balance the
bottom set?

ANSWER 195

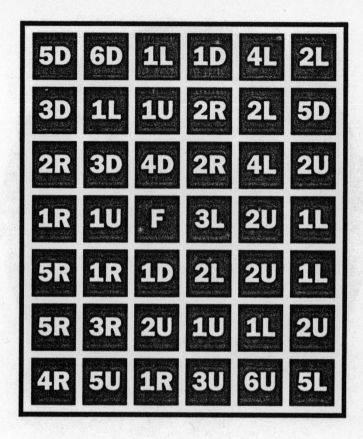

NUMBER PUZZLE 173

Here is an unusual safe. Each of the buttons must
be pressed once only in the correct order to open it.
The last button is always marked F. The number of
moves and the direction is marked on each button.
Thus 1U would mean one move up
whilst 1L would mean one move to the left.
Which button is the first you must press?

ANSWER 185

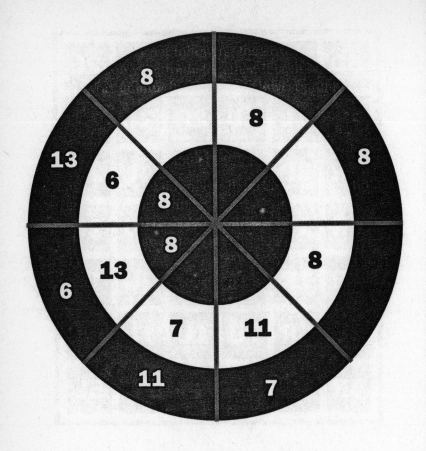

NUMBER PUZZLE 174

Complete the grid in such a way that each segment
of three numbers totals the same.
When this has been done correctly each of the three
concentric circles of eight numbers will produce
identical totals.
Now complete the diagram.

ANSWER 133

NUMBER PUZZLE 175

Start in the middle circle and move from circle to
touching circle. Collect the four numbers which
will total 53. Once a route has been found return to
the middle circle and start again.
If a route can be found, which obeys the above
rules but follows both a clockwise and an
anticlockwise path, it is treated as two different
routes. How many different ways are there?

ANSWER 175

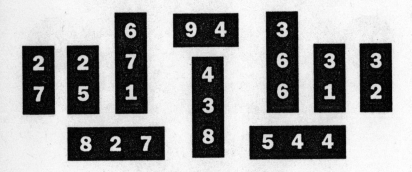

NUMBER PUZZLE 176

Place the tiles in a square to give some five-figure numbers. When this has been done accurately the same five numbers can be read both down and across. How does the finished square look?

ANSWER 123

NUMBER PUZZLE 177

Start in the middle circle and move from circle to touching circle. Collect the four numbers which will total 49. Once a route has been found return to the middle circle and start again.

If a route can be found, which obeys the above rules but follows both a clockwise and an anticlockwise path, it is treated as two different routes. How many different ways are there?

ANSWER 164

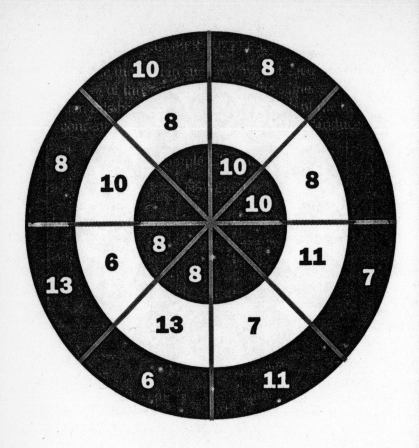

NUMBER PUZZLE 178

Each slice of this cake adds up to the same number. Also each ring of the cake totals the same. Which number should appear in the blanks?

ANSWER 271

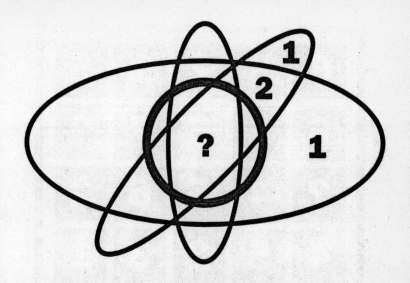

NUMBER PUZZLE 179

If you look carefully you should see why the
numbers are written as they are. What number
should replace the question mark?

ANSWER 214

NUMBER PUZZLE 180

Which number should replace the question marks
in the diagram?

ANSWER 112

NUMBER PUZZLE 181

You have five shots with each go to score 61. Aim
at this target and work out how many different
ways there are to make the score. Assume each
shot scores and once five numbers have been used
the same five cannot be used again in another
order. How many ways are there?

ANSWER 177

NUMBER PUZZLE 182

Fill up this square with the numbers 1 to 5 so
that no row, column or diagonal line of five squares
uses the same number more than once.
What number should replace the question mark?

ANSWER 270

NUMBER PUZZLE 183

Look at the pattern of number in the diagram.
What number should replace the question mark?

ANSWER 247

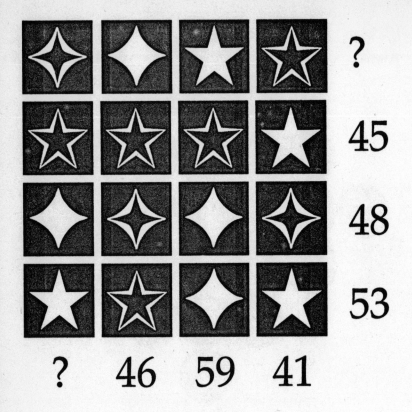

			?
			45
			48
			53

?   46   59   41

NUMBER PUZZLE 184

The contents of each box has a value. The total of the values is shown alongside a row or beneath a column. Which number should replace the question marks?

ANSWER 153

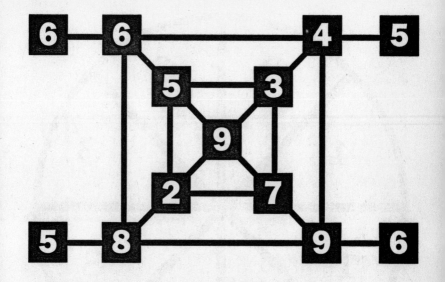

NUMBER PUZZLE 185

Start at any corner number and collect another four
numbers by following the paths shown. Add the
five numbers together.
How many times can you score 38?

ANSWER 194

NUMBER PUZZLE 186

Each sector of this wheel has a number
written on it. Using the numbers shown how
many different ways are there to add four numbers
together to make a total of 14? A number can be
used more than once, but a group cannot be
repeated in a different order.

ANSWER 269

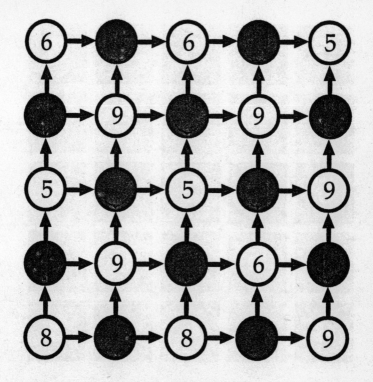

NUMBER PUZZLE 187

Move from the bottom left-hand 8 to the top
right-hand 5 adding together all five numbers.
Each black circle is worth minus 4 and this should
be taken away from your total each time you meet
one. What is the lowest total and how many
different routes are there to find it?

ANSWER 209

NUMBER PUZZLE 188

Move from square to adjacent square either vertically
or horizontally. Begin at the bottom left-hand square
and end at the top right-hand square. Collect nine
numbers and total them. How many different ways are
there to total 48?

ANSWER 142

A B C D E

A	B	C	D	E
6	2	6	4	
4	1	5	3	
6	1	7	5	4
3	1	4	2	1
8	4	6	4	0

NUMBER PUZZLE 189

There is a relationship between the columns of
numbers in this diagram. The letters above the grid
are there to help you. Which number should be
placed in the empty squares?

ANSWER 184

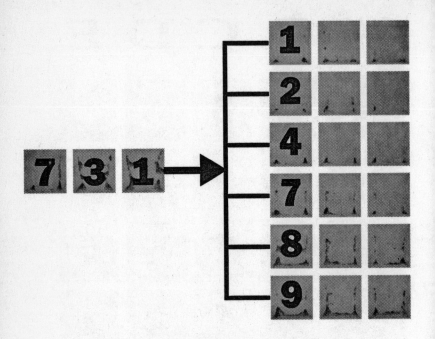

NUMBER PUZZLE 190

Place six three digit numbers of 100 plus at the end
of 731 so that six numbers of six digits are
produced. When each number is divided by 39.5
six whole numbers can be found. In this case, the
first numbers are given.
Which numbers should be placed in the grid?

ANSWER 132

NUMBER PUZZLE 191

Each row, column and five-figure diagonal line
in this diagram must total 50. Four different
numbers must be used, as many times as necessary,
to achieve this.
What are the numbers?

ANSWER 174

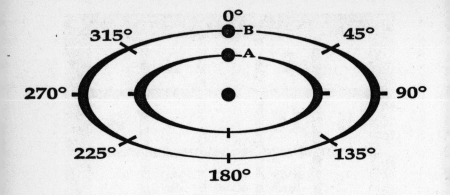

NUMBER PUZZLE 192

Two planets are in line with each other and the
sun. The outer planet will orbit the sun every
36 years. The inner planet takes 4 years. Both
move in a clockwise direction. When will they next
form a straight line with each other and the sun?
The diagram should help you.

ANSWER 122

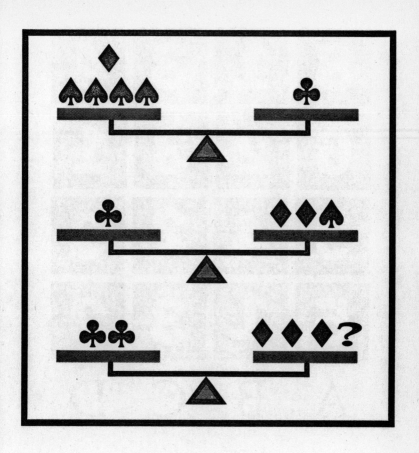

NUMBER PUZZLE 193

The top two scales are in perfect balance.
How many spades will be needed to balance the
bottom set?

ANSWER 163

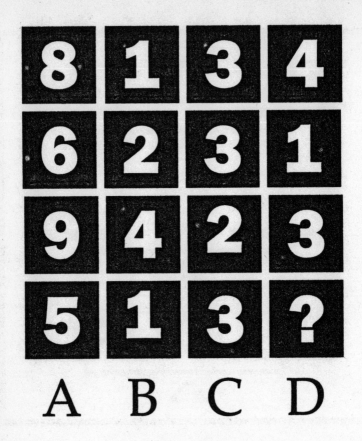

A B C D

NUMBER PUZZLE 194

The numbers in column D are linked in
some way to those in A, B and C. What number
should replace the question mark?

ANSWER 248

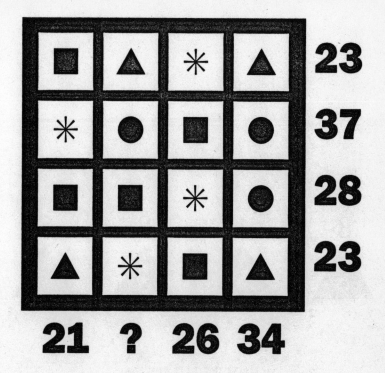

NUMBER PUZZLE 195

Each symbol is worth a number. The total
of the symbols can be found alongside each row
and column. What number should replace
the question mark?

ANSWER 253

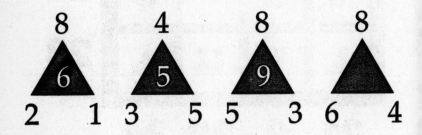

NUMBER PUZZLE 196

Which figure should be placed in the
empty triangle?

ANSWER 111

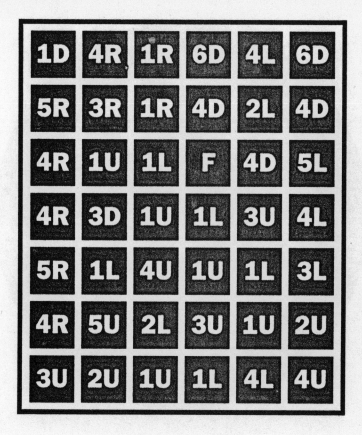

1D	4R	1R	6D	4L	6D
5R	3R	1R	4D	2L	4D
4R	1U	1L	F	4D	5L
4R	3D	1U	1L	3U	4L
5R	1L	4U	1U	1L	3L
4R	5U	2L	3U	1U	2U
3U	2U	1U	1L	4L	4U

NUMBER PUZZLE 197

Here is an unusual safe. Each of the buttons must
be pressed once only in the correct order to open it.
The last button is always marked F. The number of
moves and the direction is marked on each button.
Thus 1U would mean one move up
whilst 1L would mean one move to the left.
Which button is the first you must press?

ANSWER 146

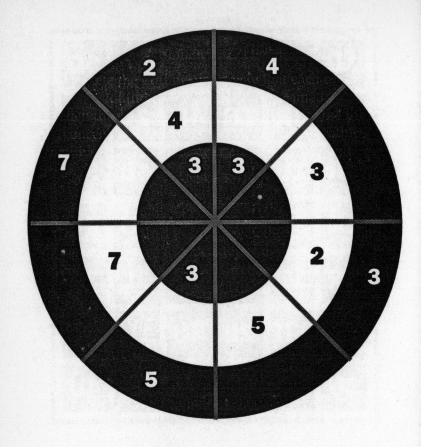

NUMBER PUZZLE 198

Complete the grid in such a way that each segment
of three numbers totals the same.
When this has been done correctly each of the three
concentric circles of eight numbers will produce
identical totals.
Now complete the diagram.

ANSWER 152

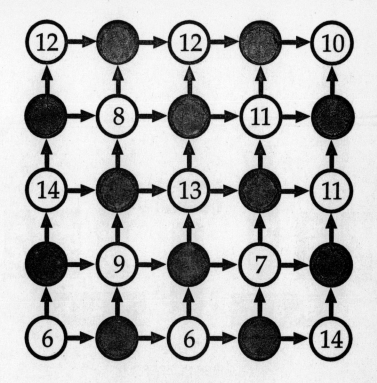

NUMBER PUZZLE 199

Move from the bottom left-hand corner to the top
right-hand corner following the arrows. Add the
numbers on your route together. If each black spot
is worth minus 7, how many different times can
you score 22?

ANSWER 193

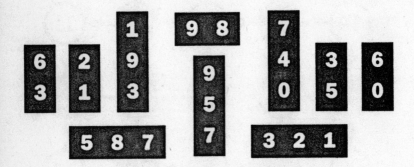

NUMBER PUZZLE 200

Place the tiles in a square to give some five-figure numbers. When this has been done accurately the same five numbers can be read both down and across. How does the finished square look?

ANSWER 141

NUMBER PUZZLE 201

Start in the middle circle and move from circle to touching circle. Collect the four numbers which will total 45. Once a route has been found return to the middle circle and start again.
If a route can be found, which obeys the above rules but follows both a clockwise and an anticlockwise path, it is treated as two different routes. How many different ways are there?

ANSWER 183

NUMBER PUZZLE 202

Which number should replace the question marks
in the diagram?

ANSWER 131

NUMBER PUZZLE 203

You have three shots with each go to score 18. Aim
at this target and work out how many different
ways there are to make the score. Assume each
shot scores and once three numbers have been used
the same three cannot be used again
in another order.
How many are there?

ANSWER 173

NUMBER PUZZLE 204

Start at the middle 5 and move from circle to touching circle. Collect three numbers and add them to the 5. How many different routes are there to make a total of 16?

ANSWER 246

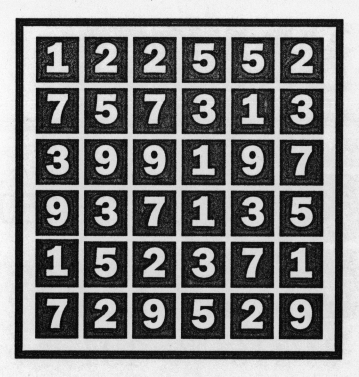

NUMBER PUZZLE 205

Divide up the box into six identical shapes. The numbers in each shape add up to the same. How is this done?

ANSWER 265

? 96 150 96

? 116 ? 104

NUMBER PUZZLE 206

The contents of each box has a value. The total of the values is shown alongside a row or beneath a column. Which number should replace the question marks?

ANSWER 121

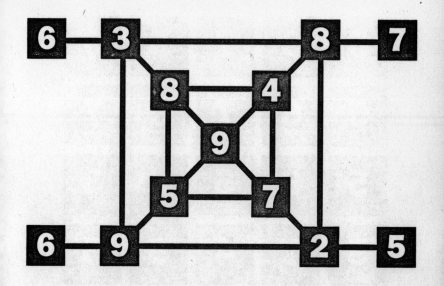

NUMBER PUZZLE 207

Start at any corner number and collect another four
numbers by following the paths shown. Add the
five numbers together.
How many ways can you score 36?

ANSWER 162

NUMBER PUZZLE 208

Move from square to adjacent square either
vertically or horizontally. Begin at the bottom
left-hand square and end at the top right-hand
square. Collect nine numbers and total them.
What is the highest score possible?

ANSWER 110

A B C D E

A	B	C	D	E
5	3	5	8	8
6	3	6	9	
6	1	4	7	5
5	1	3	6	4
5	2	4	7	6

NUMBER PUZZLE 209

There is a relationship between the columns of numbers in this diagram. The letters above the grid are there to help you. Which number should be placed in the empty square?

ANSWER 198

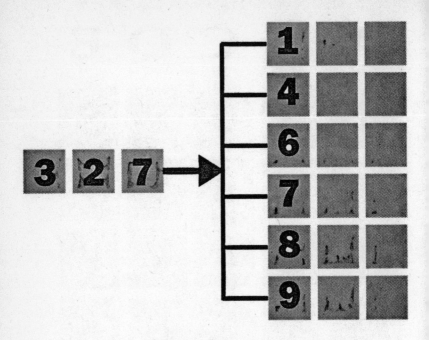

NUMBER PUZZLE 210

Place six three digit numbers of 100 plus at the end of 327 so that six numbers of six digits are produced. When each number is divided by 27.5 six whole numbers can be found. In this case, the first numbers are given. Which numbers should be placed inthe grid?

ANSWER 151

NUMBER PUZZLE 211

Each row, column and five-figure diagonal line
in this diagram must total 60. Three different
numbers must be used, as many times as necessary,
to achieve this. What are the numbers?

ANSWER 192

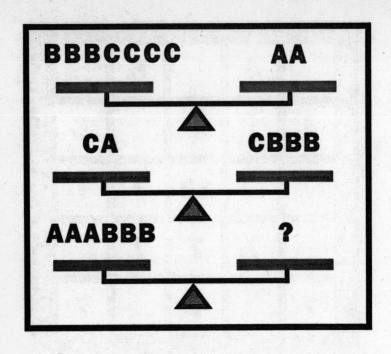

NUMBER PUZZLE 212

Scales 1 and 2 are in perfect balance.
How many Cs are needed to balance the third set?

ANSWER 257

NUMBER PUZZLE 213

How many squares of any size can you find in
this diagram?

ANSWER 211

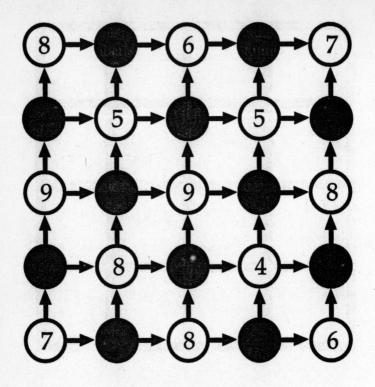

NUMBER PUZZLE 214

Move from the bottom left-hand corner to the top right-hand corner following the arrows. Add the numbers on your route together. If each black spot is worth 13, which two numbers can be scored once only?

ANSWER 140

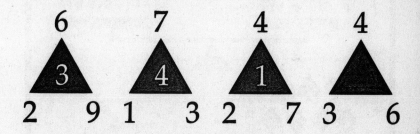

NUMBER PUZZLE 215

Which figure should be placed in the empty triangle?

ANSWER 130

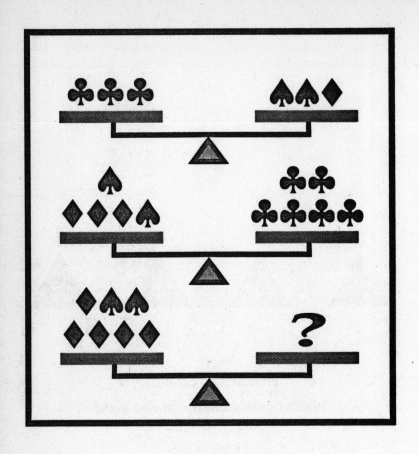

NUMBER PUZZLE 216

The top two scales are in perfect balance.
How many clubs will be needed to balance the
bottom set?

ANSWER 182

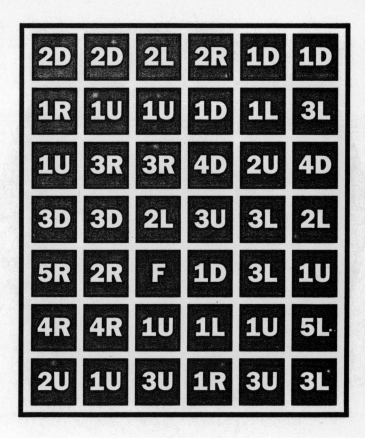

2D	2D	2L	2R	1D	1D
1R	1U	1U	1D	1L	3L
1U	3R	3R	4D	2U	4D
3D	3D	2L	3U	3L	2L
5R	2R	F	1D	3L	1U
4R	4R	1U	1L	1U	5L
2U	1U	3U	1R	3U	3L

NUMBER PUZZLE 217

Here is an unusual safe. Each of the buttons must
be pressed once only in the correct order to open it.
The last button is always marked F. The number of
moves and the direction is marked on each button.
Thus 1U would mean one move up
whilst 1L would mean one move to the left.
Which button is the first you must press?

ANSWER 172

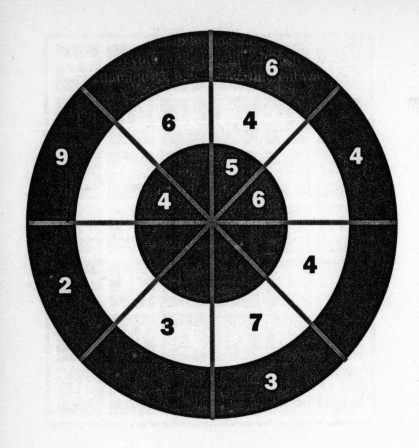

NUMBER PUZZLE 218

Complete the grid in such a way that each segment of
three numbers totals the same.
When this has been done correctly each of the three
concentric circles of eight numbers will produce
identical totals.
Now complete the diagram.

ANSWER 120

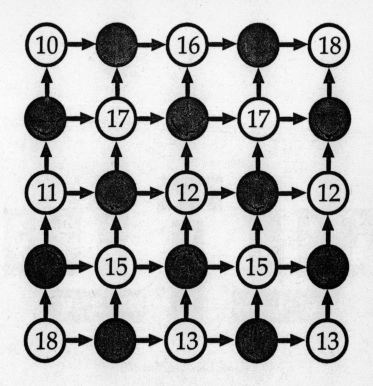

NUMBER PUZZLE 219

Move from the bottom left-hand corner to the top
right-hand corner following the arrows. Add the
numbers on your route together. If each black spot is
worth minus 9, how many times can you score 41?

ANSWER 161

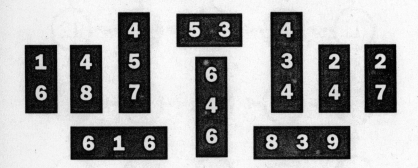

NUMBER PUZZLE 220

Place the tiles in a square to give some five-figure numbers. When this has been done accurately the same five numbers can be read both down and across. How does the finished square look?

ANSWER 109

NUMBER PUZZLE 221

Start in the middle circle and move from circle to touching circle. Collect the four numbers which will total 75. Once a route has been found return to the middle circle and start again.

If a route can be found, which obeys the above rules but follows both a clockwise and an anticlockwise path, it is treated as two different routes. How many different ways are there?

ANSWER 202

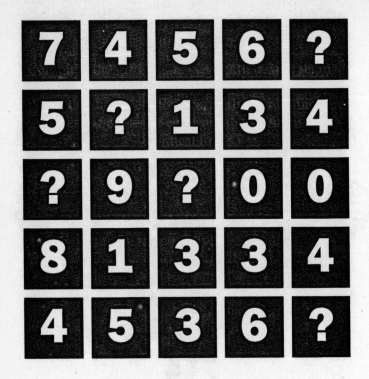

NUMBER PUZZLE 222

Which number should replace the question marks
in the diagram?

ANSWER 150

NUMBER PUZZLE 223

You have five shots with each go to score 56. Aim
at this target and work out how many different
ways there are to make the score. Assume each
shot scores and once five numbers have been used
the same five cannot be used again in another
order. How many ways are there?

ANSWER 191

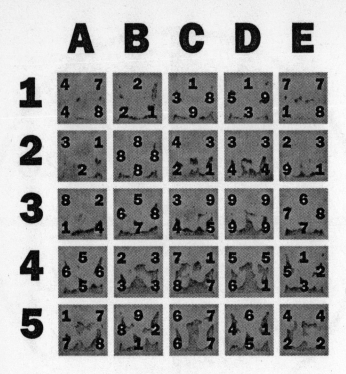

NUMBER PUZZLE 224

Which squares contain the same numbers?

ANSWER 266

NUMBER PUZZLE 225

Fill in the empty boxes, using two
numbers only, so that every line adds up to 25.
What number should replace the question mark?

ANSWER 249

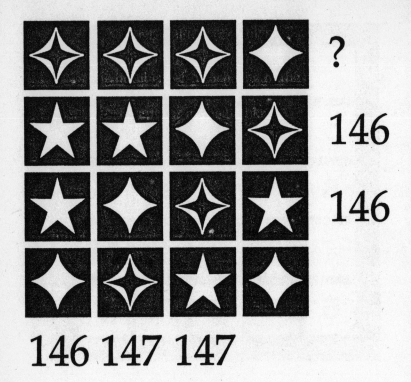

146 147 147

NUMBER PUZZLE 226

The contents of each box has a value. The total of the values is shown alongside a row or beneath a column. Which number should replace the question mark?

ANSWER 139

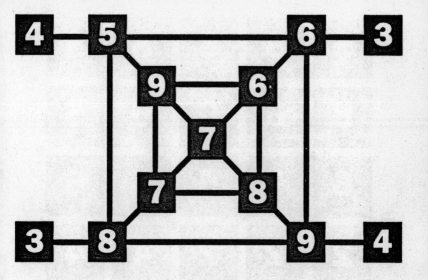

NUMBER PUZZLE 227

Start at any corner number and collect another four
numbers by following the paths shown. Add the
five numbers together. How many times can you
score less than 30?

ANSWER 181

NUMBER PUZZLE 228

Move from square to adjacent square either
vertically or horizontally. Begin at the bottom
left-hand square and end at the top right-hand
square. Collect nine numbers and total them.
What are the highest and lowest numbers you
can score?

ANSWER 129

A B C D E

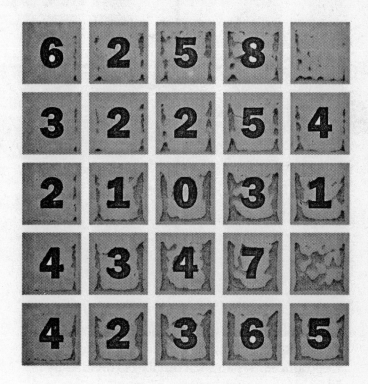

A	B	C	D	E
6	2	5	8	
3	2	2	5	4
2	1	0	3	1
4	3	4	7	
4	2	3	6	5

NUMBER PUZZLE 229

There is a relationship between the columns of
numbers in this diagram. The letters above the grid
are there to help you. Which number should be
placed in the empty squares?

ANSWER 171

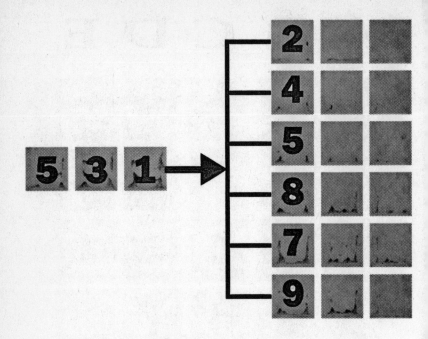

NUMBER PUZZLE 230

Place six three digit numbers of 100 plus at the end of 531 so that six numbers of six digits are produced. When each number is divided by 40.5 six whole numbers can be found. In this case, the first numbers are given. Which numbers should be placed in the grid?

ANSWER 119

NUMBER PUZZLE 231

Each row, column and five-figure diagonal line
in this diagram must total 55. Three different
numbers must be used, as many times as necessary,
to achieve this.
What are these numbers?

ANSWER 160

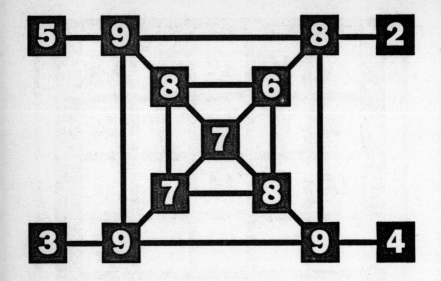

NUMBER PUZZLE 232

Start at any corner number and collect another four
numbers by following the paths shown. Add the
five numbers together.
How many times can you score 40?

ANSWER 108

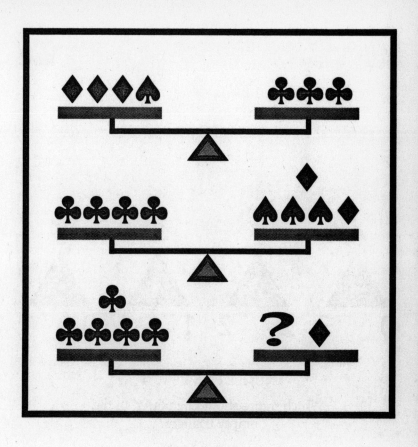

NUMBER PUZZLE 233

The top two scales are in perfect balance.
How many spades will be needed to balance the
bottom set?

ANSWER 201

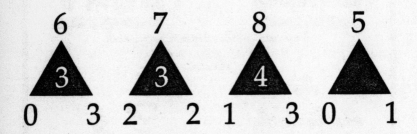

NUMBER PUZZLE 234

Which figure should be placed in the empty triangle?

ANSWER 149

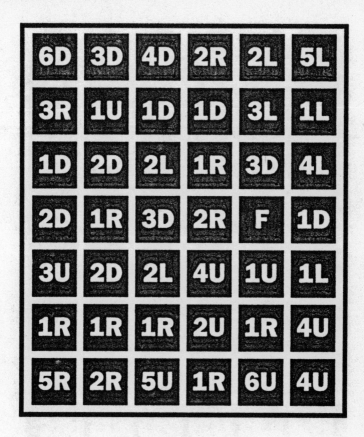

6D	3D	4D	2R	2L	5L
3R	1U	1D	1D	3L	1L
1D	2D	2L	1R	3D	4L
2D	1R	3D	2R	F	1D
3U	2D	2L	4U	1U	1L
1R	1R	1R	2U	1R	4U
5R	2R	5U	1R	6U	4U

NUMBER PUZZLE 235

Here is an unusual safe. Each of the buttons must be pressed once only in the correct order to open it. The last button is always marked F. The number of moves and the direction is marked on each button. Thus 1U would mean one move up whilst 1L would mean one move to the left. Which button is the first you must press?

ANSWER 190

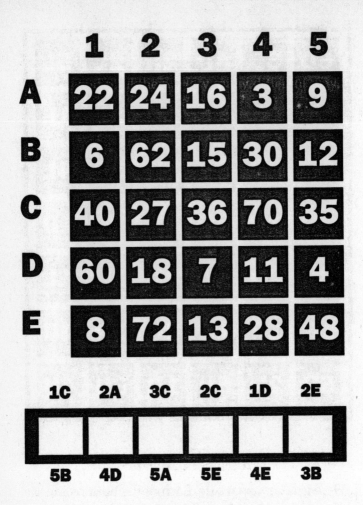

	1	2	3	4	5
A	22	24	16	3	9
B	6	62	15	30	12
C	40	27	36	70	35
D	60	18	7	11	4
E	8	72	13	28	48

1C 2A 3C 2C 1D 2E

[ ] [ ] [ ] [ ] [ ] [ ]

5B 4D 5A 5E 4E 3B

NUMBER PUZZLE 236

Find the correct six numbers to put in the frame.
There are two choices for each square, for example
1A would give the number 22. When the correct
numbers have been found a series will appear.
What is the series?

ANSWER 245

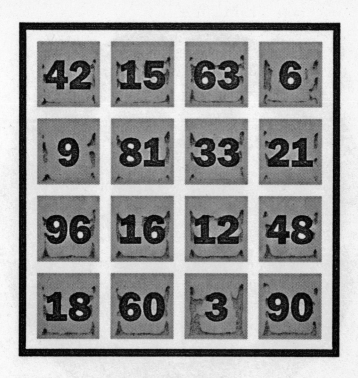

NUMBER PUZZLE 237

Which of the numbers in the square is
the odd one out and why?

ANSWER 216

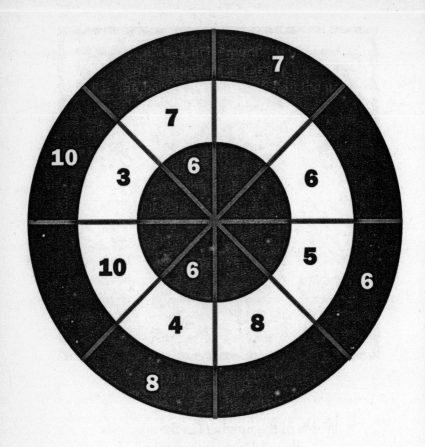

NUMBER PUZZLE 238

Complete the grid in such a way that each segment
of three numbers totals the same.
When this has been done correctly each of the three
concentric circles of eight numbers will produce
identical totals.
Now complete the diagram.

ANSWER 138

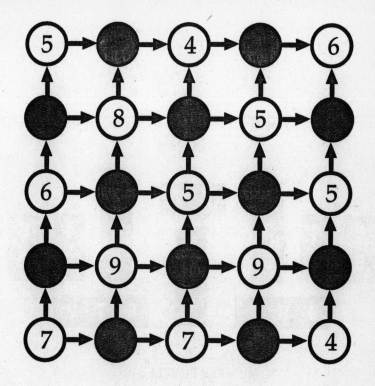

NUMBER PUZZLE 239

Move from the bottom left-hand corner to the top right-hand corner following the arrows. Add the numbers on your route together. If each black spot is worth 11, how many times can you score 80?

ANSWER 180

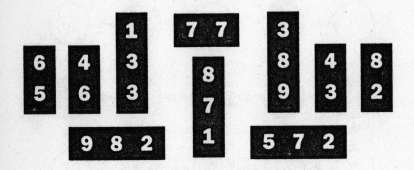

NUMBER PUZZLE 240

Place the tiles in the square to give some five-figure
numbers. When this has been done accurately the
same five numbers can be read both down and
across. How does the finished square look?

ANSWER 128

NUMBER PUZZLE 241

Start in the middle circle and move from circle to
touching circle. Collect the four numbers which
will total 83. Once a route has been found return to
the middle circle and start again.
If a route can be found, which obeys the above
rules but follows both a clockwise and an
anticlockwise path, it is treated as two different
routes. How many different ways are there?

ANSWER 170

5	4	3	0	6
8	7	6	5	2
3	3	?	4	6

NUMBER PUZZLE 242

Which number should replace the question mark in
the diagram?

ANSWER 118

NUMBER PUZZLE 243

You have five shots with each go to score 44. Aim
at this target and work out how many different
ways there are to make the score. Assume each
shot scores and once five numbers have been used
the same five cannot be used again in another
order. How many ways are there?

ANSWER 159

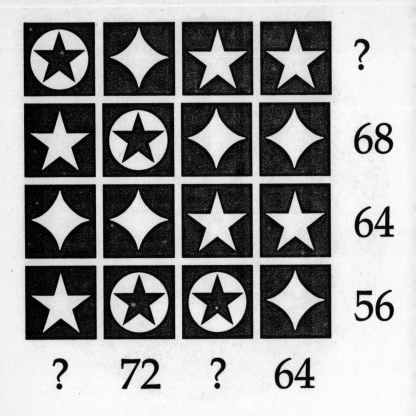

NUMBER PUZZLE 244

The contents of each box has a value. The total of the values is shown alongside a row or beneath a column. Which number should replace the question marks?

ANSWER 107

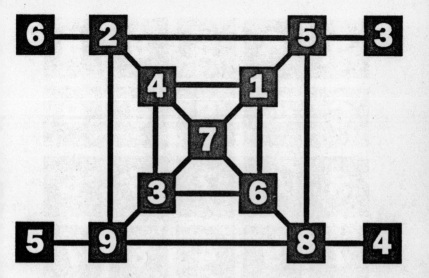

NUMBER PUZZLE 245

Start at any corner number and collect another four
numbers by following the paths shown. Add the
five numbers together.
What is the lowest number you can score?

ANSWER 200

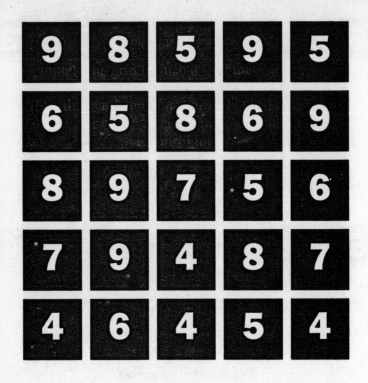

NUMBER PUZZLE 246

Move from square to adjacent square either
vertically or horizontally. Begin at the bottom
left-hand square and end at the top right-hand
square. Collect nine numbers and total them.
Which total can be scored only once?

ANSWER 148

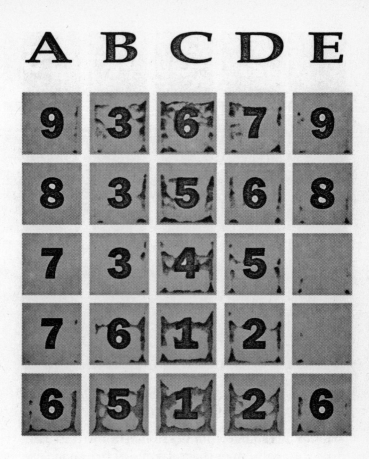

NUMBER PUZZLE 247

There is a relationship between the columns of numbers in this diagram. The letters above the grid are there to help you. Which number should be placed in the empty squares?

ANSWER 189

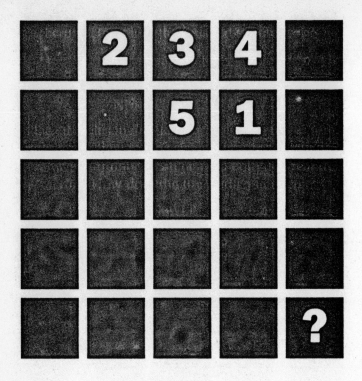

NUMBER PUZZLE 248

Fill up this square with the numbers 1 to 5 so that
no row, column or diagonal line of five squares
uses the same number more than once. What number should replace the question mark?

ANSWER 252

NUMBER PUZZLE 249

Look at the pattern of numbers in the diagram.
What number should replace the question mark?

ANSWER 221

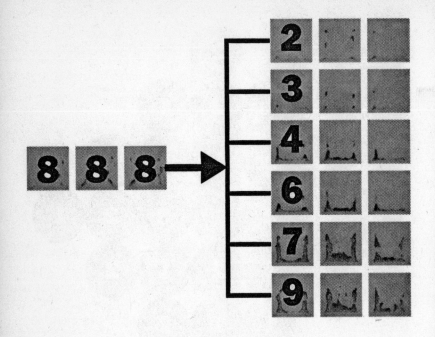

NUMBER PUZZLE 250

Place six three digit numbers of 100 plus at the end of 888 so that six numbers of six digits are produced. When each number is divided by 77 six whole numbers can be found. In this case, the first numbers are given. Which numbers should be placed inthe grid?

ANSWER 137

NUMBER PUZZLE 251

Each row, column and five-figure diagonal line in this diagram must total 40. Three different numbers must be used, as many times as necessary, to achieve this.

What are the numbers?

ANSWER 179

NUMBER PUZZLE 252

Start in the middle circle and move from circle to touching circle. Collect the four numbers which will total 62. Once a route has been found return to the middle circle and start again.
If a route can be found, which obeys the above rules but follows both a clockwise and an anticlockwise path, it is treated as two different routes. How many different ways are there?

ANSWER 127

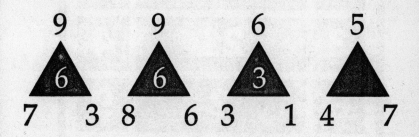

NUMBER PUZZLE 253

Which figure should be placed in the
empty triangle?

ANSWER 117

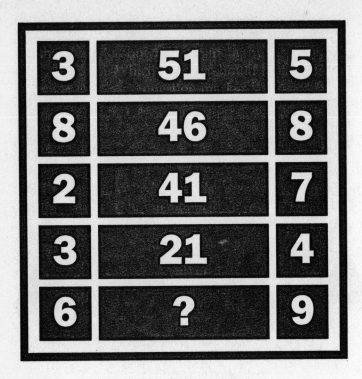

3	51	5
8	46	8
2	41	7
3	21	4
6	?	9

NUMBER PUZZLE 254

The numbers in the middle section have some
connection with those down the sides. Find out
what it is and tell us what should
replace the question mark?

ANSWER 242

NUMBER PUZZLE 255

Move up or across from the bottom left-hand 5 to
the top right-hand 3. Collect nine numbers and add
them together. What is the highest you can score?

ANSWER 263

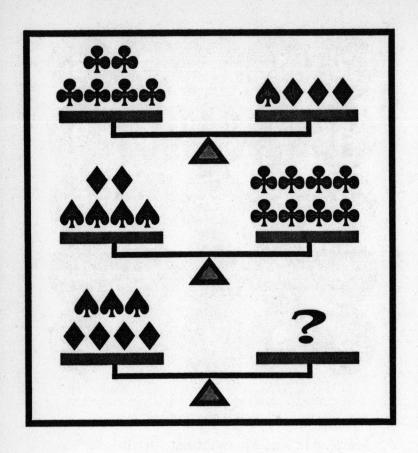

NUMBER PUZZLE 256

The top two scales are in perfect balance.
How many clubs will be needed to balance the
bottom set?

ANSWER 169

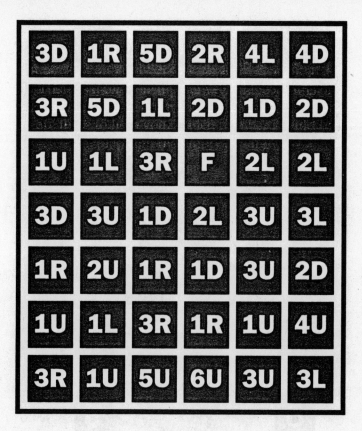

3D	1R	5D	2R	4L	4D
3R	5D	1L	2D	1D	2D
1U	1L	3R	F	2L	2L
3D	3U	1D	2L	3U	3L
1R	2U	1R	1D	3U	2D
1U	1L	3R	1R	1U	4U
3R	1U	5U	6U	3U	3L

NUMBER PUZZLE 257

Here is an unusual safe. Each of the buttons must
be pressed once only in the correct order to open it.
The last button is always marked F. The number of
moves and the direction is marked on each button.
Thus 1U would mean one move up
whilst 1L would mean one move to the left.
Which button is the first you must press?

ANSWER 158

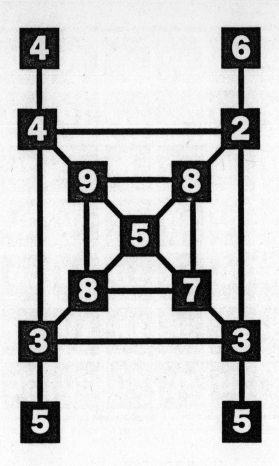

NUMBER PUZZLE 258

Start at any corner and follow the lines. Add up the
first four numbers you meet and then add on the
corner number. What is the lowest possible total
and how many different routes lead to it?

ANSWER 268

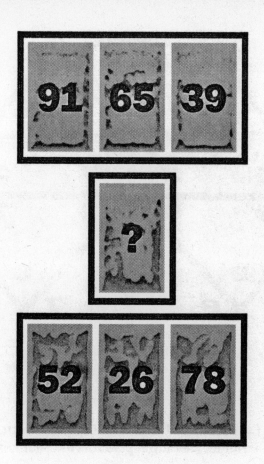

NUMBER PUZZLE 259

Place in the middle box a number larger than 1.
If the number is the correct one, all the other
numbers can be divided by it without leaving any
remainder. What is the number?

ANSWER 218

NUMBER PUZZLE 260

Each sector of the circle follows a pattern.
What number should replace the question mark?

ANSWER 223

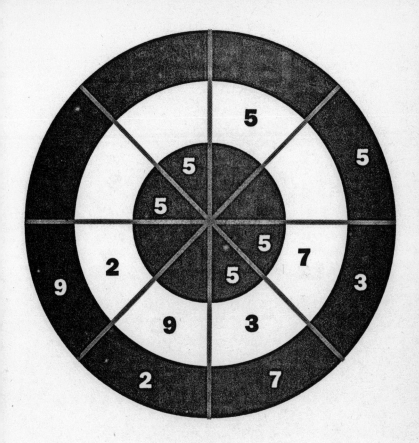

NUMBER PUZZLE 261

Each slice of this cake adds up to the same number.
Also each ring of the cake totals the same. Which 2
numbers should appear in the blanks?

ANSWER 250

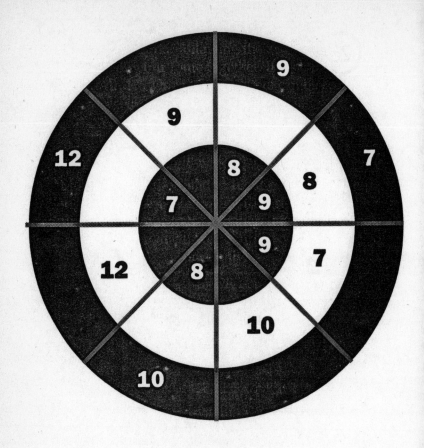

NUMBER PUZZLE 262

Complete the grid in such a way that each segment
of three numbers totals the same.
When this has been done correctly each of the three
concentric circles of eight numbers will produce
identical totals. Now complete the diagram.

ANSWER 106

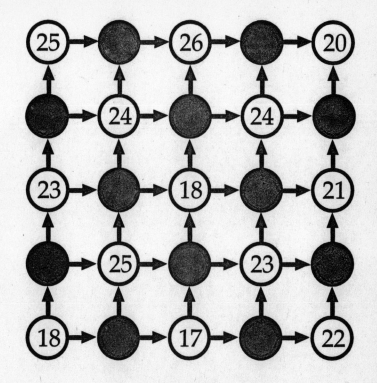

NUMBER PUZZLE 263

Move from the bottom left-hand corner to the top right-hand corner following the arrows. Add the numbers on your route together. If each black spot is worth minus 19, how many times can you score 24?

ANSWER 199

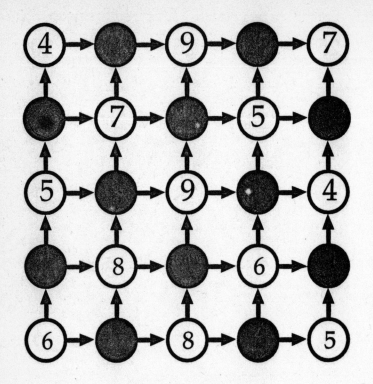

NUMBER PUZZLE 264

Move from the bottom left-hand 6 to the top
right-hand 7 adding together all five numbers.
Each black circle is worth minus 5 and this should
be taken away from your total each time you
meet one. How many different routes, each
giving a total of 10, can be found?

ANSWER 228

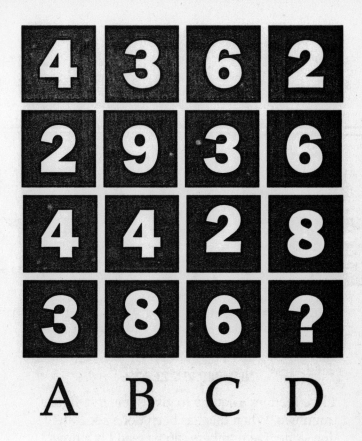

A B C D

NUMBER PUZZLE 265

The numbers in column D are linked in some way
to those in A, B and C. What number should
replace the question mark?

ANSWER 272

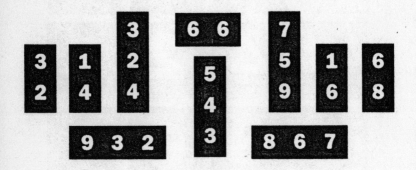

NUMBER PUZZLE 266

Place the tiles a square to give some five-figure numbers. When this has been done accurately the same five numbers can be read both down and across. How does the finished square look?

ANSWER 147

NUMBER PUZZLE 267

Start in the middle circle and move from circle to touching circle. Collect the four numbers which will total 90. Once a route has been found return to the middle circle and start again.
If a route can be found, which obeys the above rules but follows both a clockwise and an anticlockwise path, it is treated as two different routes. How many different ways are there?

ANSWER 188

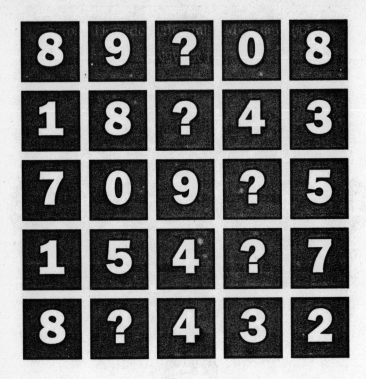

NUMBER PUZZLE 268

Which number should replace the question marks
in the diagram?

ANSWER 136

NUMBER PUZZLE 269

You have three shots with each go to score 36. Aim
at this target and work out how many different
ways there are to make the score. Assume each
shot scores and once three numbers have been used
the same three cannot be used again in another
order. How many are there?

ANSWER 178

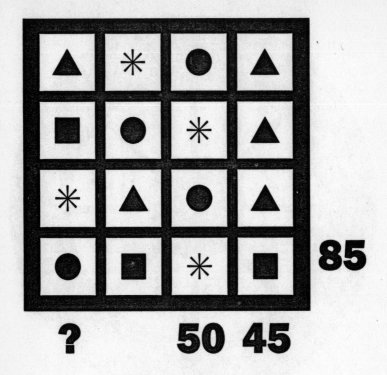

85

? 50 45

NUMBER PUZZLE 270

Each symbol is worth a number. The total
of the symbols can be found alongside a row and
two columns. What number should replace
the question mark?

ANSWER 234

NUMBER PUZZLE 271

Start at the middle 9 and move from circle to touching circle. Collect three numbers and add them to the 9. How many different routes are there to make a total of 17?

ANSWER 225

The contents of each box has a value. The total of the values is shown alongside a row or beneath a column. Which numbers should replace the question marks?

ANSWER 126

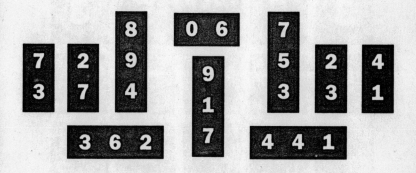

NUMBER PUZZLE 273

Place the tiles in a square to give some five-figure numbers. When this has been done accurately the same five numbers can be read both down and across. How does the finished square look?

ANSWER 168

NUMBER PUZZLE 274

Move from square to adjacent square either
vertically or horizontally. Begin at the bottom
left-hand square and end at the top right-hand
square. Collect nine numbers and total them.
How many different ways are there to total 39?

ANSWER 116

A	B	C	D	E
9	0	6	9	
8	1	6	9	7
7	2	6	9	8
7	1	5	8	
3	1	1	4	2

NUMBER PUZZLE 275

There is a relationship between the columns of numbers in this diagram. The letters above the grid are there to help you. Which number should be placed in the empty squares?

ANSWER 157

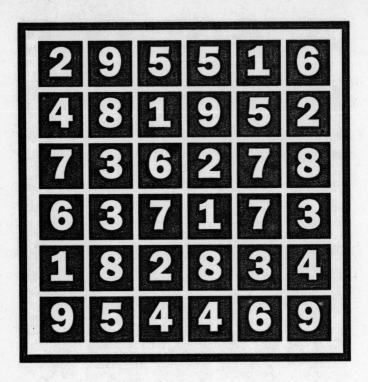

2	9	5	5	1	6
4	8	1	9	5	2
7	3	6	2	7	8
6	3	7	1	7	3
1	8	2	8	3	4
9	5	4	4	6	9

NUMBER PUZZLE 276

Divide up the box into four identical shapes.
The numbers in each shape add up to the same.
How is this done?

ANSWER 256

NUMBER PUZZLE 277

How many rectangles of any size can you find in this diagram?

ANSWER 261

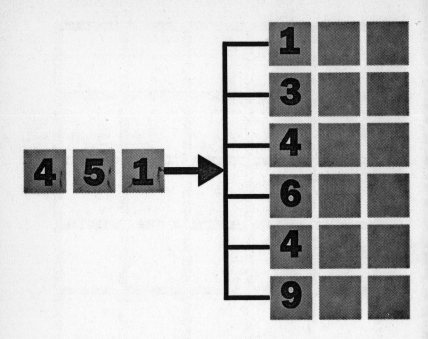

NUMBER PUZZLE 278

Place six three digit numbers of 100 plus at the end of 451 so that six numbers of six digits are produced. When each number is divided by 61 six whole numbers can be found. In this case, the first numbers are given. Which numbers should be placed in the grid?

ANSWER 105

The
BRAINTEASERS
Number
Puzzles
Book

ANSWERS

1. 17.

2.

3. 29.

4. 10. The top number is multiplied by the bottom left-hand number and the total is divided by the bottom right-hand number.

5. 1. The top row minus the bottom row gives the third row. The bottom row plus the second row gives the fourth row.

6. 164
295
426
557
688
819

7. Our answer is:

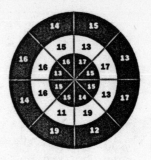

8. 11 ways.

9. In two years time. The outer planet is 60 degrees in its orbit, the sun is in the middle and the inner planet is at 240 degrees.

10.

11. 8. The top row minus the bottom row gives the third row. The third row plus the second row gives the fourth row.

12. 131
264
397
663
796
929

13. Our answer is:

14. 107 (values of symbols:
◈ = 18, ◆ = 30,
☆ = 29).

15. Once.

16.

17. Once.

18. 7. The top number is multiplied by the bottom left number and the bottom right number is taken away from this total to give the middle number.

19. 5. 3rd row - top row = 5th row. 4th row + 5th row = 2nd row.

20. 162
313
464
615
766
917

21.

22. Three times.

23. 4. The top number is added to the bottom left-hand number and the bottom right-hand number is subtracted.

24. 6. The top row plus the second row gives the third row. The second row plus the fourth row gives the fifth row.

25. 314
425
536
647
758
869

26. Our answer is:

27. 149 (values of symbols: ◈ = 35, ◆ = 42, ☆ = 37).

28. 3 times.

29.

30. 3 ways.

31. Our answer is:

32. 65 (values of symbols: ✪ = 7, ◆ = 8, ★ = 25, ☆ = 17).

33. In three and three-quarter years' time. The outer planet is 90 degrees in its orbit, the sun is in the middle and the inner planet is at 270 degrees.

34.

35. Once.

36. 3. The top number minus the bottom left-hand number is multiplied by the bottom right-hand number.

37. 1. The second row plus the third row gives the top row. The third row plus the fourth row gives the bottom row.

38. 431
542
653
764
875
986

39. Our answer is:

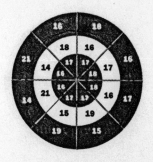

40. 62 (values of symbols: ⊠ = 13, ★ = 21, ◆ = 7).

41. 6 ways.

42. 7 clubs.

43. 8. The middle row minus the bottom row equals the top row.

44. 232
354
476
598
842
964

45. Our answer is:

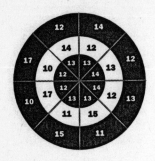

46. 78 (values of symbols:
⬡ = 28, ✩ = 13,
▣ = 9).

47. In one and a half years'
time. The outer planet is
90 degrees in its orbit,
the sun is in the middle
and the inner planet is at
270 degrees.

48.

5	5	5	3	1
5	6	7	7	2
5	7	8	4	5
3	7	4	2	6
1	2	5	6	8

49. 2 ways.

50. 6. The bottom two numbers are added and taken
from the top number.

51. 5. Take the bottom row
from the middle row to
give the top row.

52. 27 ways.

53. 0, 1 and 4.

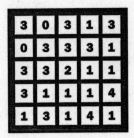

54. Four.

55. 40.

56. 4 spades.

57. 10 ways.

58. 2. A + B = D.
A - B = C.
D - C = E.

59. 4U on the third row from the bottom.

60. 204 (values of symbols: ☆ = 44, ✪ = 58, ✧ = 45).

61. 10, 11, 23 and 31.

25	9	23	5	23
12	22	24	23	4
24	20	17	14	10
13	11	10	12	39
11	23	11	31	9

62. 5 routes.

63. 14 ways.

64. 4. A + B = D.
A - B = C.
D - C = E.

65. 1L in the second column from the left one row from thebottom.

66. 8 ways.

67. 9, 17 and 18.

19	12	18	4	17
13	17	19	18	3
18	20	14	8	10
9	10	9	11	31
11	11	10	29	9

68. Four routes.

69. 30.

70. 7 clubs.

71. 12 ways.

72. 2. A + B = D.
A - B = C.
D - C = E.

73. 58.

74. 40 and once.

75. 6 clubs.

76. 7 ways.

77. 4. A - B + 1 = D.

D - 1 = C.

D + B - 1 = E.

78. 1L in the third column from the left on the third row from the bottom.

79. 15 ways.

80. 11, 12 and 21.

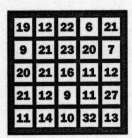

19	12	22	6	21
9	21	23	20	7
20	21	16	11	12
21	12	9	11	27
11	14	10	32	13

81. 4 times.

82. 37.

83. 1U in the second column from the left on the second row.

84. 7 ways.

85. 9 and 17.

17	10	17	4	17
8	17	19	17	4
17	22	13	4	9
14	9	7	9	26
9	7	9	31	9

86. 2 routes.

87. 4 times.

88. 4 diamonds.

89. 7 ways.

90. 3. A - B = D.

C = D + 2.

E = D - B.

91. 1D fourth from the left on the top row.

92. 11 ways.

93. 27 and twice.

94. 3. The top number minus the bottom left-hand number minus the bottom right-hand number.

95. 7 ways.

96. 5. A - B = D.
D + 2 = C.
D - B = E.

97. 3U on the bottom row.

98. 21 ways.

99. 11, 18 and 19.

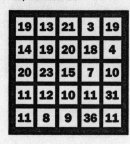

100. One.

101. Twice.

102. 5 clubs.

103. 5 ways.

104. 157 (values of symbols: ★ = 45, ✦ = 44, ☆ = 23).

105. 156
339
461
644
400
949

106. Our answer is:

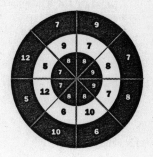

107. 52 (values of symbols: ★ = 12, ☆ = 8, ✦ = 24).

108. 3 times.

109.

110. 60.

111. 8. The top number minus the bottom left–hand number multiplied by the right–hand number.

112. 8. 3rd row - top row = 5th row. 5th row + 4th row = 2nd row.

113. 233
356
479
725
848
971

114. Our answer is:

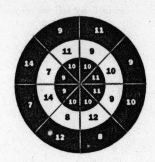

115. 217
366
515
664
813
962

116. 2 ways.

117. 7. The top number minus the bottom left–hand number multiplied by the right hand number.

118. 3. Top row + bottom row = middle row.

119. 279
441
522
846
765
927

120. Our answer is:

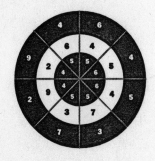

121. 122 (values of symbols:
⊠ = 20, ☆ = 24,
★ = 42, ✩ = 36).

122. In 2 ¼ years time. The
outer planet is 22.5
degrees in its orbit, the
sun is in the middle and
the inner planet is at
202.5 degrees.

123.

124. 2 ways.

125. 1, 3, and 4.

126. 126 at the side and 122
beneath (values of symbols:
☆ = 31, ◆ = 30, ✪ = 35).

127. 11 ways.

128.

129. 58 and 37.

130. 6. The top number multiplied
by the bottom left–hand
number minus the right–hand
number.

131. 5. The top row plus the second row gives the third row. The second row plus the fourth gives the fifth row.

132.
145
224
461
777
856
935

133. Our answer is:

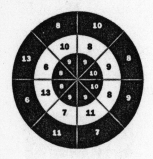

134. 53 (values of symbols: ☆ = 4, ✪ = 17, ✦ = 15).

135. 4 routes.

136. 6. 2nd row + 3rd row = top row. 3rd row + 4th row = 5th row.

137.
272
349
426
657
734
965

138. Our answer is:

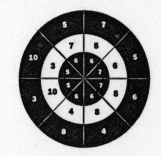

139. 148 (values of symbols: ✦ = 38, ☆ = 37, ◆ = 34).

140. 90 and 92.

141.

1	9	3	2	1
9	5	7	6	3
3	7	4	0	5
2	6	0	9	8
1	3	5	8	7

142. 4 ways.

143. 5. The top number is added to the bottom left–hand number and the bottom right–hand number is subtracted.

144. 3. The top row is the total of the 2nd and 3rd rows. The bottom row is the total of the 3rd and 4th rows.

145. 4 ½. The top number multiplied by the bottom left–hand number divided by the bottom right–hand number.

146. 5U on the second row from the bottom.

147.

148. 54.

149. 4. The top number minus the two bottom numbers combined.

150. 2. The top row minus the bottom row gives the third row. The third row plus the second row gives the fourth row.

151. 195
415
635
745
855
965

152. Our answer is:

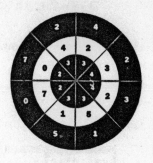

153. 47 (values of symbols ⬙ = 6, ★ = 11, ☆ = 12, ◆ = 18).

154. 2 ways.

155.

156. In twelve and a half years time. The outer planet is 45 degrees in its orbit, the sun is in the middle and the inner planet is at 225 degrees.

157. 6. A + B = D.
D − 3 = C. C + B = E.

158. 3U on the bottom row.

159. 34 ways.

160. 7, 8 and 15.

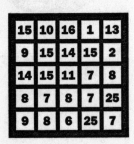

161. Once.

162. 2 ways.

163. 5 spades.

164. 9 ways.

165. 8. A − B + 1 = D.
D − 1 = C.
B + C = E.

166. 3D on the top row.

167. 1. A + B − 1 = D.
D − 3 = C.
B + C = E

168.

169. 10 clubs.

170. 7 ways.

171. 7. A + B = D.
D – 3 = C.
C + B = E.

172. 3R in the third column
fromthe left on the third
row down.

173. 7 ways.

174. 8, 12, 13 and 14.

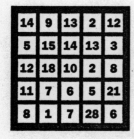

175. 19 ways.

176. 4 times.

177. 37 ways.

178. 9 ways.

179. 5, 8 and 11.

180. 8 times.

181. 6 times.

182. 9 clubs.

183. 7 ways.

184. 2. A – B = D.
D + 2 = C.
D – B = E

185. 2R on the third row
down in the fourth col-
umn from the left.

186. 59 ways.

187. 3, 4 and 6.

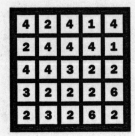

188. 13 ways.

189. 7. A − B = C.
C + 1 = D.
B + C = E.

190. 4U on the third row from the bottom.

191. 21 ways.

192. 15, 17 and 24.

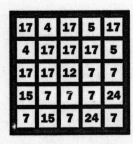

193. 8 times.

194. Once.

195. 3 diamonds.

196. 7 ways.

197. 7 clubs.

198. 9. A + B = D.
D − 3 = C.
C + B = E..

199. Once.

200. 15.

201. 5 spades

202. 4 ways.

203. 8 in the outer section at the top, 3 in the outer section below and 5 in the inner one.

204. 4.

205. 2.

206. 32. It is the only even number.

207.

208. 23.

209. 13 and one way.

210. 6. The number down the right-hand side is taken from the the number down the left-hand side to give the number in the middle section.

211. 55.

212. 1 3 6 10 15 21. The numbers increase by 2, 3, 4, etc.

213. 3B and 1D.

214. 4. The number is found in 4 overlapping shapes.

215. 22.

216. 16. All the other numbers are divisible by 3.

217. 1. Each sector's total increases by 1.

218. 13.

219. 7. Add together A, B and C to get D.

220. 1i, found between 4A and 3C.

221. 1. The total of each horizontal line doubles from the outside to the centre.

222. 23.

223. 9. Each sector in the bottom half of the circle totals double its opposite.

224. 2C, 3B and 4A.

225. 12.

226. 50.

227. 21.

228. 5.

229. 1 3 5 7 9 11.
The numbers increase by 2 each time.

230. 14. All the other numbers are divisible by 4.

231. 2 3 5 7 11 13. These are all prime numbers.

232. 3. Opposite sectors total the same.

233. 100.

234. 60.

235. 5.

236.

237. Each pair of numbers on each row total 20. The first two on the bottom row, 2 and 10, do not.

238. 8.

239. 22.

240. 11.

241. 2S, in the fourth column.

242. 45. The numbers down the sides are multiplied together to give the number in the middle section, placed in a reversed order.

243. 7.

244. 7.

245. 12 24 36 48 60 72. The numbers increase by 12 each time.

246. 13.

247. 4. The total of each horizontal line doubles from the outside to the centre.

248. 1. A minus B minus C gives D.

249. 7.

250. 4 and 6.

251. 2. The number down the left-hand side is divided by the number down the right-hand side to give the number in the middle section.

252. 3.

253. 30.

254. 41.

255. 18.

256.

257. 16.

258. 20.

259 . 4.

260. 9. Each column of numbers totals 9.

261. 225.

262. 9.

263. 47.

264. 6.

265.

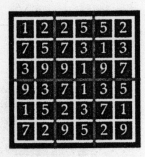

1	2	2	5	5	2
7	5	7	3	1	3
3	9	9	1	9	7
9	3	7	1	3	5
1	5	2	3	7	1
7	2	9	5	2	9

266. 1E, 4C and 5A.

267. 0 and 6.

268. 16 is the lowest and there are 2 routes.

269. 23.

270. 3.

271. 9.

272. 4. A times B divided by C gives D.

273. 4.

274. 6. Add together A and B, then take away C in order to get D.

275. 1C.

276. 10.

277. 1.

278. 4.

NOTES

NOTES

NOTES

NOTES

NOTES

NOTES

NOTES

NOTES

NOTES

NOTES

NOTES

NOTES

NOTES

NOTES

NOTES

NOTES